EX LIBRIS

John H. T. Mc Pherson, Jr.

Forward Surgeon

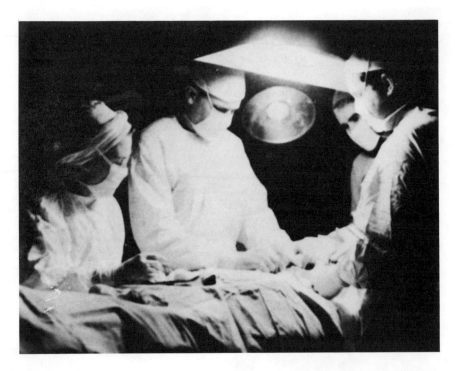

General Surgical Team No. 15 at Work January 1944, on Mount Lungo in Mignano Gap. Left to right: Mosher, Wolff, Westerfield, and Adkins.

FORWARD SURGEON

The Diary of
Luther H. Wolff, M.D.,
Mediterranean
Theater,
World War II,
1943–45

VANTAGE PRESS
New York / Washington / Atlanta
Los Angeles / Chicago

"Courage of Wounded Soldiers Remarkable," by Lee McCardell, and extracts from *Surgeon to Soldier,* by Dr. Edward D. Churchill, were reprinted by permission.

FIRST EDITION

Published by Vantage Press, Inc.
516 West 34th Street, New York, New York 10001

Manufactured in the United States of America
ISBN: 0-533-06288-8

Library of Congress Catalog Card No.: 84-90249

To my wife, Mary Will (Giles) Wolff

Contents

Foreword

Forward Surgeon is a war story of blood and guts, literally. It is of a battle fought by the medics. This is a story of one surgeon's courageous and stark record. This is a story of upfront, on the battle lines—a surgeon battling under fire to save lives. For intense, selfless devotion to duty, the experience of army surgeons has no equal in modern medical battlefield experience. To read these day-to-day, short, rugged, pithy lines as noted in this diary leaves one exhausted, taut, and emotionally wrung dry.

A great admiration and thankfulness is felt for the medical teams that day after day on major pushes by the infantry outfits they supported trudged on. Field hospitals were immediately behind the division medics, sometimes in front of the division command post in exposed areas. It is exciting; it is exhilarating; it is a story one finds difficult to stop reading. This telling of the medical battle is a story of suspense. It is a story that should be read if one is to have full knowledge of World War II battlefields. It is an accurate, eyeball-to-eyeball account, on-the-scene accounting, by a skillful, professional MD, a dedicated surgeon, performing a humanitarian service for mankind under horrid conditions—rugged mountainous terrain, wretched weather, rain, snow, wind, and cold, and shrapnel—all death-dealing.

Only the medics themselves know the depth of the demands on the physical as well as the mental pressures, of the problems facing them when a major battle is on and the wounded are two to a cot in all the tents and it is continuous operating around the clock—exhaustion—"fall in my bunk with my clothes on."

The wounded soldier, the GI, his reaction under fire, under stress of battle, his courage—his no-complaining—his great relief to find a haven in the field hospital when wounded—his confidence in the medics on the operating table is magnificent—the GI is the best patient of all.

Rain and rain, constant in the Apennines, snow, cold, these rugged mountains a great obstacle to the military in their efforts to move forward—the medics suffered, too, but kept going.

This story has great suspense—compassionate appeal. There is frequent movement of the medical installations, forward, closer to the guns—to the divisions they are supporting. One can feel the tumult of war and dive with the medics for the foxhole, shells shrieking overhead—the crunch of the big ones close by, shrapnel through the tents, the stench of rotting flesh, long-delayed dressing wounds, the pathos of the amputated legs and arms, the patience and courage of the wounded—all this and a catnap and then back at it again—this is the story that grips the emotions, strips one of fear, of fatigue; the medics go on and on, keep operating, saving lives, no glorious acclaim for their great effort to fight off death—and there are so many when a major push is on.

Today it is exhaustion; tomorrow will be the same; it will bring more mangled bodies for the surgeons to put back to some semblance of life.

A challenge—this is the incentive to go on and on. What a challenge!

Maynard R. Ashworth
Publisher Emeritus
Columbus Ledger-Enquirer

Preface

In the fall of 1973 during an air flight to the West Coast, I took along my old World War II diary, which I had not opened in twenty-eight years. After this lapse of so many years, the diary proved interesting to me and to my wife and I resolved to reorganize it a bit and have it typed for my childlren's edification as well as to give them some insight into that phase of my life of which they had little knowledge.

The diary itself is presented virtually verbatim with only an occasional elaboration (in italics). Unfortunately, there were many incidents, amusing and otherwise, that would have enlivened the diary considerably from personality aspects, though there was always the thought lurking in my subsconscious that should I have gotten killed, my relics would have been censored. Hence I went easy on some of the more personal and spicy occurrences. I cannot explain at this time the curious gap in the diary from January 14, 1945 to April 22, 1945; nor can I explain to what "It sure is nice to look ahead———" (April 22, 1945) refers. Strictly from memory and from my "V" mail letters, which I had sent almost daily to my wife, Mary Will, I have endeavored to fill in some of the gaps in the prologue and epilogue sections, regretting that I did not write them down when the events took place.

Happily, being somewhat of a map nut, I marked locations and dates on acquired military maps, so I was able to reconstruct accurately the geography involved. As regards the photographs, I am deeply indebted to Dr. George Donaghy (Gorgeous George) of Leesburg, Florida, and to Dr. Paul Kennedy (The General) of Hillsborough, California, who supplied me with most of these items.

For their recent invaluable encouragement and advice, I am most grateful to Glenn Vaughn, publisher of the *Columbus Ledger-Enquirer*, and to Maynard R. Ashworth, publisher emeritus of the same paper.

Salerno beachhead scene. Burning bulldozer hit by 88. D day, September 9, 1943.
Courtesy of "D Day" Taylor

Introduction

Prior to World War II, practically all patients with severe wounds of the abdomen and thorax were permitted to die with no operative intervention. During World War I, the hospitals were established well behind the front lines and were more or less stationary units. Again, there was little definitive surgery performed on belly or chest wounds. The patient either died (the usual outcome) or got well (rarely) on his own. However, toward the end of World War I, the concept of having experienced surgical teams perform surgery on the severely wounded forward in the division area developed and was tried out on a limited scale. This proved to be so successful that it led to the planning during World War II of mobile surgical hospitals to be staffed by experienced and well-trained surgeons working far forward within the division area. The plans provided for auxiliary surgical groups, four of which were activated during World War II. The Second Auxiliary Surgical Group was the first group to be activated and sent to a theater of operations (the Mediterranean). When the invasion of North Africa occurred in November of 1942, an advanced detachment of the Second Auxiliary Surgical Group went along. Unfortunately, no one in Africa had ever heard of an auxiliary surgical team and they didn't know exactly what to do with them. Three teams landed at Algiers on D Day and were finally moved up to the Tunisian front, where they saw very limited operative surgical service in division clearing stations and evacuation hospitals directly supporting the fighting front. Obviously, from their reports, there was general confusion and disorder, and the teams were much like lost sheep, with no one particularly wanting them or knowing what to do with them.

During the Sicilian campaign of Patton's Seventh Army, things worked out better. Mobile field hospitals had arrived, and surgical teams were widely used in them. Each field hospital was divided into three platoons: one platoon was set up adjacent to the division clearing station, and at least four surgical teams and two shock teams from the Auxiliary Surgical Group worked in these active operating platoons.

With the rapid movement encountered, the field hospital platoons would leapfrog forward, the same surgical teams moving up to the more advanced location. Because of the brevity of the Sicilian campaign, many problems still remained, and it was not until the second month of the Italian campaign that forward surgery began to work out with maximum efficiency and effectiveness. Field hospitals were routinely set up five to ten miles behind the front lines, well within artillery range of the enemy. Only the most severely wounded were treated in the field hospitals; the bulk (about 90 pecent) of the wounded were sent directly from the clearing station back to the evacuation hospitals, which were located five to twenty miles behind the field hospitals.

Col. James H. Forsee, our commanding officer, had the foresight and vision to require all surgeons to keep detailed records of all cases and to send reports of these cases to Headquarters every few weeks. Even before we went overseas, suitable forms and follow-up forms were devised and we were all issued ledger-type books in which operative records were immediately recorded. These records were transferred to Headquarters forms during the less hectic periods. At the completion of hostilities, the group had detailed data on 3,154 cases of abdominal wounding, 2,267 cases of chest wounding, including 903 thoraco-abdominal wounds, 1,028 traumatic amputations, 5,438 compound fractures, and a similar proportion of other severely wounded.

Colonel Forsee asked me (the same as ordered me) to be editor-in-chief of the Second Auxiliary Surgical Group's report to the surgeon general. This wound up by being the greatest collection of detailed data on war wounds ever compiled and largely formed the professional basis of *Medical History of World War II,* published by the surgeon general in 1955. This report took four months to complete.

Prologue

February 20, 1942, was a poignant and sad day for me. At about 3:00 P.M., I told my wife, children, and other close relatives good-bye, knowing that I would be gone for months, years, or even forever. Mary Will, my dear wife, looked as if her world were coming to an end, and I am sure I looked the same. Fortunately, at the last heartbreaking moment, our little daughter, Mary Louise, age four, provided the comic relief that was desperately needed at the time by chirping, "Dad, when you come back, bring me a present." She had to wait almost three years for that present, poor kid.

I still recall how despondent and depressed I was after the train left Roanoke. I do not ever remember being so low in spirits before or after. During the first hour after leaving Roanoke, I sat gazing out the window. The sky was crystal clear. As the train glided toward Bedford, the ridges of the Blue Ridge were silhouetted against the sky on the right. The peaks of Otter loomed to the left. Tree trunks of various shades of gray, brown, and black stretching up the ridges caught my eye. The stark, bare branches of the trees were silhouetted against the evening sky in a lacy pattern. The thoughts kept racing through my mind: *Will I ever see this beautiful country again? Will I ever feel the love of my wife and children? Will I ever get to know our unborn child?* And on and on.

I recovered from this slough of despond in due time and arrived the next morning at Camp Kilmer, New Jersey, which was our overseas staging area. Camp Kilmer was one the minor horrors of the war—rows on rows on rows of identical two-story wooden barracks surrounded by mud, dirty snow, wind, and nothing to do. We were "staged" (i.e., instructed), which requires a couple of hours; then we sat for almost a week on "Red Alert" with nothing to do except to get into one of the poker or crap games that went on twenty-four hours a day or else read, which I did, a book a day. Enough whiskey was smuggled in so that there were a couple of riotous parties to break the ennui of waiting. Finally, on February 27, 1942, we were shepherded aboard a long troop train, each man carrying his Val-Pac, duffle bag, and musette bag. We had arrived at a dock in New York just after dark and walked about a mile carrying the same impedimenta, finally boarding the S. S. *Andes,* of British registry. The *Andes* was used formerly as a luxury liner in the South American–European trade. Each stateroom was now occupied by eight officers in stacked bunks; the enlisted men were quartered below decks in four-tiered bunks.

About daylight the next morning, the ship was pushed from her berth and then dropped anchor in the harbor just beyond the Statue of Liberty. We sat there all day watching the New York skyline, the Statue of Liberty, and the bustling activity of the harbor. At dusk, we weighed anchor, steamed out into the Atlantic, and headed about due south. It was cold and rough the first night, but being allowed on deck under strict blackout, I went out to see what I could see. There was absolutely no sign of any escort vessels or convoy. Querying one of the British ship officers brought the reassuring (??) information that we were too fast for convoy and that we were going it alone, and this was at the peak of the U-boat offensive!

We continued on a due south course all the next day, the seas getting continually more boisterous. By dinnertime—that is, the evening meal—all my roommates were developing a peculiar green color and were either moaning in bed or dashing to the head with dreadful wretching and vomiting. Having no such symptoms and seeking more pleasant companionship, I made my way to the elaborate and ornate officers' dining room, where a veritable corps of British waiters attended about twenty-five of us who felt like eating. The rest of the 400-plus officers never made it to the dining room that evening.

By the next morning, the sea was calm and filled with golden brown seaweed. The air temperature was a balmy eighty degrees or so, and the British officers had broken out their white uniforms, complete with white shorts. We uncivilized Americans were still in our winter wools and hot! The ship proceeded in an easterly zigzag direction at about twenty-five knots. I assumed that we were in the Sargasso Sea, which was a lot better than being in the North Atlantic. The trip was very pleasant thereafter. Mild excitement developed one day while we were eating lunch. Without warning, dishes and tableware, our chairs and people standing slid and fell simultaneously toward the starboard side. A great clatter of broken china and glasses, heaps of human-occupied chairs, and various other peculiar sounds and sights were produced almost simultaneously. It was explained later that a lookout called a torpedo track on the starboard, and I wouldn't have ever believed that a ship this big could turn to port so abruptly! The lookout's warning was, fortunately, erroneous.

About the eighth day out, a good old Catalina flying boat circled and dipped her wings to us. We had not seen a ship, plane, or other manmade objects since we left the New Jersey coast. The presence of this boat told us we were approaching our destination and that someone must actually know our whereabouts! Much cheering and laughter ensued.

On March 9, 1943, we disembarked at Casa Blanca, Morocco, which is an aptly named city—all houses and buildings are white. We were quartered in various hotels, schools, and pyramidal tents and had no duties except for reporting in daily. We quickly acquired bicycles and spent the days riding about the city and environs. I even tried fishing in the Atlantic, with dismal results.

On March 20, 1943, this group was moved to Rabat, where we set up tents in the infield of a racetrack. Here we continued our physical-fitness program and the training instructions for enlisted men.

Several things impressed me most about Rabat:

(1) The intense cold of the nights, partially alleviated by setting three or four Primus gasoline stoves aflame after dark so that we could play gin rummy, poker, and checkers in our tents by candlelight. I was in the same tent with Johnny Adams, George Donaghy, and Trogler Adkins *(Maj. John E. Adams of Charlottesville, Virginia, orthopedist, Maj. George E. Donaghy of Boston, Massachusetts, anesthetist for Johnny Adams, and Capt. Trogler F. Adkins of Durham, North Carolina, my assistant surgeon).*

(2) The plague of locusts. For about three days, these large pink-and-yellow grasshoppers, about three inches long and capable of prolonged flight, flew through, over, and around our camp by the millions or perhaps billions. They all flew from the east toward the west, straight for the Atlantic Ocean. It soon became apparent to those of us athletically inclined that here was an inexhaustible supply of live badminton shuttlecocks streaming by. Therefore, we fashioned paddles out of wood, and for three days there would be anywhere from ten to twenty officers lined up in our company street furiously flailing at these invaders, the objective being to prevent any of the locusts from passing down the company street. We never accomplished this objective (there were just too many of them), but it was great fun and exercise. Incidentally, the natives gather great basketsful of these locusts, sun dry them, and eat them as a great delicacy. I didn't!

(3) The night of the Atabrine. We were introduced to this great and recently discovered antimalarial drug one night after supper when we were lined up and each given two Atabrine tablets to take then and there. Within an hour, just at dark, numbers of people were seen running to the latrines or standing outside their tent retching and vomiting. The nausea, vomiting, and diarrhea were so severe and prostrating that two

or three jeeps and command cars made continuous runs under blackout conditions from the living tents to the latrines, transporting those too sick to walk. Fully two-thirds of the group were so afflicted, and all in all it was a terrible night. Luckily, I was not adversely effected by this drug.

(4) The Sultan's Guard. Almost daily, this company of gaudily and colorfully clothed men, astride beautiful horses, paraded past our camp with much pomp, ruffles, and flourishes. A very impressive sight, indeed.

(5) Two nurses' casualties: our first known nurse pregnancy and a severe round burn of the buttocks caused by her dropping a lighted cigarette between her legs while seated on a latrine seat—some idiot had put gasoline in the pit to keep down flies and odors!

(6) We have an Olympic class snorer in our tent in the form of George Donaghy. Due to the reverberations of George's snoring, the only way Johnny Adams can sleep is for him to lie on his side and to plug the upper ear canal with the cap off the filling plunger of his fountain pen.

In 1975, I revisited Rabat, staying at the Rabat Hilton Hotel. Inquiries regarding the racetrack there were met with blank stares or negative gestures. Finally, someone mentioned the Hippodrome about four blocks away. I walked over to it and immediately recognized it as the old racetrack where we had stayed, despite the huge new concrete stands and the conversion of the racetrack into a steeplechase track. In 1943, this track, was out in the country, and now it is completely surrounded by high-rise apartments and other buildings.

After about three weeks in Rabat, we were herded aboard a train for the trip to Oran. The rail line ran inland in an easterly direction. We passed through many Arab villages and town including Fez and Sidi-Bel-Abbes, the headquarters of the French Foreign Legion. The snow covering the mountains was plainly visible to the southeast, a very curious sight from the hot, dry desert through which we were passing.

Arriving at Oran, we were transported to a hot, miserable hill southeast of Oran and told to put up pup tents as living quarters. This fine location had absolutely no shade. It was a dusty, bare, and rocky ground with small, whitish scorpions everywhere. These scorpions were apparently harmless, since no one was stung, even though we had to shake them out of our blankets and bedrolls each morning. Our food consisted of C rations only. *These C rations were one of the army's early mistakes. Enclosed in a small tin can, they consisted of three flavors— that is, a stew, beans, and hash. They were designed to provide about 4,000 calories per day and were literally swimming in grease. After a day or two, even the heartiest stomachs began to rebel at this food. The subsequently issued K rations were an improvement but were not all that good.* This hill on which we were located became known as the infamous "Billy Goat Hill," and there developed as near a mutiny of the outfit, as could be imagined. Herb Moore and I acquired bicycles somewhere, and we spent our days peddling to the Arab villages securing eggs, chickens, onions, and whatever else we could obtain. We would turn this provender over to Capt. Tony Emmi and Capt. Dom Zurlo, who were skilled at cooking and fixing edibles. Every evening we would gather in their twelve-by-twelve tent (made from several pup tents) and have a "feast." One evening after we had been living in this hellish location for about five days, Colonel Forsee dropped in on us at this gathering place. No one came to attention, no one asked him to partake of the goodies, and he was really totally ignored. We were all sore as hell at him for allowing us to be put in this terrible place. I guess the message got through, for he was gone about three days and we moved immediately thereafter to a nice villa on the coast, located at Ain-el-Turk, about twenty miles southwest of Oran. This villa was used as headquarters and recreation building. We were quartered in pyramidal tents just behind the villa. This proved to be an exceptionally fine location; we swam in the wonderful Mediterranean water two or three times daily, played games, and drank horrible vino rouge—a thoroughly delightful period in general. It was here in the first part of June that I finally heard that I was the proud father of a son, Luther Horn Wolff, Jr., born May 14, 1943. It seemed utterly fitting that I throw a party in celebration, so that with the okay of the colonel, and with the cooperation of those esteemed scroungers, Maj. Leon Fitzpatrick and Capts. Tony Emmi and Dom Zurlo, I issued the appropriate orders and posted them on the bulletin board. (See page xx.) This party was a notable success, enjoyed by everyone, apparently. We even had an unplanned comedy act, which was one of the funniest sights I have ever seen in my life.

About an hour after the party started and just before sundown, our attention was attracted to the cobblestone drive that ran directly below the terrace from the street down to the beach. The attraction was provided by two very drunk, staggering British sailors, who were supporting—or actually dragging—between them a third British sailor who had passed out. They were singing snatches of a bawdy British song and cursing and yelling, feeling no inhibitions whatsoever. Proceeding down the steep incline toward the beach, they became suddenly aware of the people at the party above them leaning over the iron railing laughing at them. They became indignant, and after some uncomplimentary remarks and repartee, they suddenly lost their balance and all three toppled over a four-foot retaining wall into some shrubbery (no doubt thorny) of the villa next door. This caused howls of laughter from the assembled spectators, but the show was not over. One of the sailors managed to climb back up on to the driveway, and while he tugged to get the passed-out guy up onto the drive, the third one pushed from below. Alas, everyone lost their balance again and landed in the shrubbery in a heap the second time. Undeterred, a second attempt was made, with the same tangled mass of humanity winding up in the shrubbery. By this time, three or four more sailors had arrived in a fairly sober state. They dragged and pushed the original three back up on the driveway, all of this to the accompaniment of every other word "bloody" and "fucking," which seem to be the only words the British sailors know.

Detachment, 2nd Auxiliary Surgical Group
12th General Hospital
APO 700

6 June 1943

TO: OFFICERS AND NURSES, 2nd AUXILIARY SURGICAL GROUP, APO 534.

1. In compliance with par. 3, a, (1), (e) Auxiliary Surgical Regulations No.1 113-16943, dated April 13, 1943 as amended in Directive No. 63, dated 29 May 1943, the facts hereinafter are brought to the attention of all concerned.

2. In accordance with the provisions of par. 1, this communication, dated 6 June 1943, it is directed pursuant to instructions received 29 May 1943 that all personnel concerned in this memorandum report without delay on the evening of 8 June 1943, Tuesday, at 2000 hours to the Terrace, Group Headquarters, 2nd Auxiliary Surgical Group.

3. Upon arrival personnel concerned will report to Major Luther H. Wolff, M.C., ASN 0-30000003, who will deliver sealed, secret orders, the aforementioned orders being unsealed by corkscrews only.

4. These secret orders noted under par. 3 above, will be issued for the commemoration of the following victorious event, viz., the successful and glorious termination of the 3rd Stork Campaign on 14 May 1943, in which Major and Mrs. Luther H. Wolff were awarded a son, Luther H., Jr., weight 8 pounds 12 ounces.

5. Personnel concerned, receiving sealed secret orders, will be relieved at such time as to enable them to reach their original station by 2300 hours 8 June 1943, unless the exigencies of the situation prevent their traveling except via litter or ambulance.

6. The personnel concerned: W.P., T.D.N., T.B.W.Y.C., B.Y.C.C.: R.N.G.

xx

By Command of THE GENERAL, Mrs. Luther H. Wolff:

/S/ Luther H. Wolff

Luther H. Wolff,
Major, M. C.
Executive Officer.

OFFICIAL:

(x)
Luther H. Wolff, JUNIOR
Adjutant.

1st Ind.

The procurement and assignment of supplies necessary to properly
commemorate the aforesaid victory is due to the valiant efforts
of Major Fitzpatrick, Lt. Emmi and Lt. Zurlo.

Key:
W.P.: Will Proceed
T.D.N.: Travel directed is necessary
TBWYC: Travel the best way you can
BYCC: BRING YOUR CANTEEN CUP
RNG: Results not guaranteed

The members of my party were really rolling on the floor from
laughter.

We were at Ain-el-Turk for about a month, then moved to Algiers,
bivouacking a couple of miles east of Maison Blanche. Algiers is quite
a French city, complete with a real casbah and modern hotels. We took
in the sights, sounds, and smells.

While we were stationed here, a very long ammunition train blew
up in the marshaling yards at Maison Blanche—we had a grandstand
seat for this awe-inspiring sight. Fishing in the Mediterranean was
lousy at this location. After about a week, the outfit boarded a train
for Bizerte, and on July 14, 1943, we bivouacked in a nice grove of
olive trees about ten miles west of Bizerte. We were adjacent to a
hospital row set up to care for the Sicilian Campaign casualties. Several
of the team assisted the staffs of these various evacuation and station
hospitals in the vicinity. This was a pleasant and peaceful time.

We took all of our sheets, socks, et cetera, to Tunis, where these
items were much in demand (e.g, twenty dollars for a sheet). Some of
the boys did a thriving business, but I only went once with two spare

sheets. I still liked to sleep between sheets. We also made excursions to Carthage, Ferryville, et cetera, but mostly we just loafed and played.

Almost every night or so there was an air raid over the Bizerte harbor with German planes coming over at maximum altitude. There must have been several hundred antiaircraft searchlights around the harbor, and antiaircraft guns by the hundreds also. Dozens of barrage balloons guarded the lower altitudes. It was a real fireworks show to see all the A.A. guns and the searchlights open up, streams of red tracers all over, and sky bursts of 90 mm stuff higher than the Bofors could reach. It was an awesome sight to see one of the searchlights pick up a German bomber. Every other searchlight would focus on the same plane and every gun fire at it. The plane looked like a tiny, silvery moth caught in the apex of these brilliant beams. Sometimes the bombers got away, but I saw several plunge to earth, the searchlights and guns following them right down to the ground. One such plane hit about a mile from us, and there was a good bit of flack fragments dropping around. One can always tell a German bomber by the sound of the unsynchronized motors, absolutely characteristic. I suppose the Germans decided that bombing Bizerte didn't pay, for the raids became less and less frequent as time went on. This was the greatest concentration of antiaircraft fire and searchlights I saw in the entire war, by far.

One valuable asset I derived from this period: I had a *National Geographic* with sky maps in it, and the stars in Africa, particularly with the strict blackout and the clear atmospheric conditions prevailing, were so bright and near that they seemed only a few thousand feet up. No wonder the stars played such an important part in the ancient countries of the Mediterranean! Well, I would study a constellation in the sky map in my tent by flashlight, then go outside to study it in the sky. I got to know at a glance most of the major stars and constellations, and this has helped me many times in determining directions and thereby orienting myself.

The latter part of August arrived, and I started keeping a diary.

Forward Surgeon

SCHEMATIC DIAGRAM OF CASUALTY EVACUATION

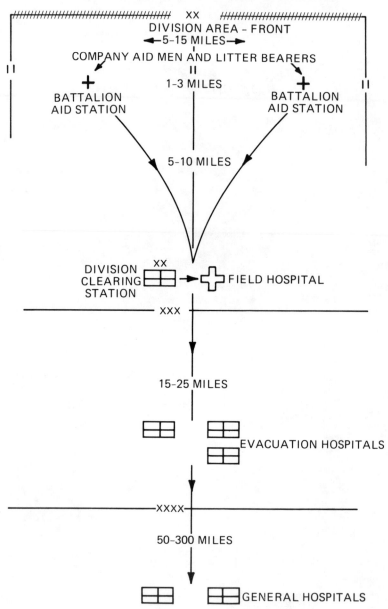

Chapter I
Salerno to Cassino

August 22, 1943—Bizerte Area

Col. James H. Forsee called us in today and told us to get ready to go places. The general surgical teams alerted are: Maj. James H. Sullivan, Milwaukee, Wisconsin; Maj. Frank W. Hall, Cape Girardeau, Missouri; Maj. Harold (Sorehead) Poole, Spartanburg, South Carolina, and Maj. Forrest E. Lowery, Ohio; orthopedic surgical teams alerted are Maj. John H. Adams and Maj. Howard Shorbe. Great activity in getting chests and supplies ready.

August 26, 1943—En route Bizerte to Oran by train

Was awakened at 2:30 A.M. Ate breakfast and loaded on a six-by-six truck. Left bivouac area and taken to the railroad station in Mateur. Yellow air raid alert on the way to Mateur though nothing came of it. Left Mateur at about 8:00 A.M. Officers and nurses in the second class coaches, all others, including Negro quartermaster batallion, in forty-by-eight freight cars. We went through Beja and east of Beja saw much evidence of battle with burned-out tanks, trucks, and so forth, left over from the Tunisian campaign. Very slow progress with hours of waiting on the sidings. Everyone thoroughly dirty. Am in compartment with Adkins, Adams, Donaghy, and Lowery. Spent most of the day playing gin rummy with Trogh Adkins and took a severe beating. Some of the local melons of rather curious types are absolutely delicious. Slept on the seats and floors with one blanket but slept surprisingly well.

August 27, 1943—En route

Arrived at El Kroub about dark. Johnny Adams and I watched a British soccer game for a half an hour or so and then went into town, purchasing eggs, tomatoes, melons, and onions, which helped out our inevitable C rations considerably. Still taking a fearful beating in gin rummy from Adkins. So dirty now, nothing matters as far as sanitation is concerned. Several severe GI upsets among personnel. The nurses are piled up in the car ahead of us and are in worse shape than we are. As is typical of all French plumbing, their "john" ceased to function within a few hours after they started from Mateur, and since then there is no other place to go, they continued to use it. Now, with the

1

diarrhea developing, there is a dreadful odoriferous situation. Whew!

August 28, 1943—En route to Oran

Proceeding by fits and starts but mostly by stops. Last night when bedtime came we were retired to our compartment. Frosty was on one seat, Adams on the other, Donaghy on the floor between them, and I in the aisle just outside the door. Soon Johnny started hollering, "There is something dead in here!" The horrible stench soon engulfed me, also. Flashlights were found and a search for the origin of the nauseating odor began. One whiff of George Donaghy's feet and the mystery was solved. With no baths or other bathing facilities, George had the worst case of bromidrosis (stinking feet) I have ever encountered. Water from canteens with some soap and scrubbing and jettisoning his socks out the door enabled us to get some sleep, finally.

August 29, 1943—En route to Oran

Had a remarkable run last night and arrived in marshaling yards outside of Algiers at 9:00 A.M. Stayed only a couple of hours and then pulled out for Oran. Managed to mail some letters to M.W. by giving them to a passing soldier. Arrived at Affreville, Meliana, at 6:00 P.M. and went into the village getting peaches and eggs. Trogh and Johnny got four huge melons that were simply delicious. Thick yellow skins but very sweet. This town is somewhat fascinating to me and would make a good place to visit. It overlooks a huge and apparently very fertile valley.

August 30, 1943—Oran

We arrived in Oran at about 3:00 P.M., much the worse for wear. Met by Col. Huddleston, Second Corps surgeon, who told us everything was loaded but us. No transportation was available so we waited around the railroad yards until about midnight. We are able to bum some coffee and French toast from a railroad outfit who were doing a swell job with the equipment available. This railroad outfit practically saved our lives with their hospitality. Spent about two hours killing time by playing pitch penny with Johnny and Sorehead Poole. Was a great loser at first but finally came out considerably ahead. This site is about eight miles west of Arzew. This Mediterranean water is surely swell. The beach is wonderful. Two swims today. Shorbe, our senior officer, is trying desperately to find something out about our future, but no one knows anything. A pyramidal tent was pitched to get us out of the broiling sun. We are messing with the collecting company of Sixteen Medical Regiment, and the food is very good. Also, an adjacent large vineyard has unlimited delicious ripe grapes! Fresh fruits and vegetables are sorely missed.

September 1, 1943

We were told to get all our equipment ready for loading, so we sat around in the broiling sun all day. This afternoon Captain Sessions of the 142nd Combat Team came out and at least found us. All equipment was loaded on trucks and pulled out this evening, but we are left with what we can carry. I found an old torn cot and patched it up with bailing wire. It certainly beats sleeping on the ground with only a blanket.

September 2, 1943—On the beach west of Arzew

We went down to Headquarters at 142nd Clearing Station this evening and tried to get transportation. We did find out that Johnny Adams's team, Lemmer's shock team, and my team were assigned to the 142nd Clearing Station to go aboard the *Marnix Van Sint Aldogande*, a Dutch ship. We had no transportation to get to this ship. After supper, we happened to spot an ensign in a six-by-six truck with navy markings, so with his permission, we all piled on and were taken directly to the dock, which was a swell break. Incidentally, all day we sat in the sun without mess facilities, water, or transportation. On arriving at the ship, we were assigned to a cabin with Johnny Adams, connecting with a cabin in which George Donaghy stays. Swell soft water shower and are we making use of it! The *Marnix* is a Dutch ship, East Indies trade, 20,000 tonner and furnished in the heavy and elaborate style of the 1890s. The food is good, and the ice cold lemonade, ginger ale, and so forth are simply wonderful.

September 3, 1943—Mers El Kabir Harbor

Troops of the thirty-sixth Infantry Divison were loading all day today. We took it easy playing gin rummy, checkers, and bridge. Our equipment is still on a lighter alongside and getting very rough handling. These beds are swell to sleep on, although it gets awfully hot with the portholes closed at night. Two men from the ninety-fifth Evac Hospital, a Major Coulter from Iowa, and Major Fouchet from Columbia, South Carolina, are our roommates.

September 4, 1943—Mers El Kabir Harbor

Still in harbor, everything loaded and quiet, but somewhat tense. We had steak three times today.

3

September 5, 1943—At sea

We moved out of the harbor at Mers El Kabir at 9:00 A.M. and lay at anchor at Oran Bay until 4:30 P.M. when the convoy started. There are twenty-two merchants, LSTs, and freighters in the convoy with twenty-six escort vessels, mostly flak ships, Corvettes, and destroyers, but there are also six heavy cruisers. Off Arzew about 6:30 P.M., then lost sight of land.

September 6, 1943—At sea

A Lieutenant Colonel Palmer, assistant surgeon of 2 Corps, briefed us briefly today. Lt. Col. "Beartracks" Palmer is a regular army officer. He is about twenty-six years old, tall, gangly and had an "Ichabod Crane" appearance with markedly oversized feet. During the North African campaign, some GI woodsmen with tracking knowledge saw his tracks in the sand of a beach and started screaming,"There is a bear here." Palmer was thereafter referred to only as Beartracks among the Mediterranean theater personnel. Anyhow, during the briefing, Beartracks told us that we were to be assigned to the 404th Clearing Station. We are to land at 3:30 A.M. about ten miles south of Salerno, Italy, the British landing to the north. The fifth Army's function is to secure the southern flank at the bridgehead.

Anyhow at the finish of the formal briefing by "Beartracks," Johnny Adams, our senior officer, started asking "Beartracks" questions about transportation, supplies, and locations. "Beartracks" flared up at Johnny and told him that he had not asked for us and did not want us. He further informed us that we would do a lot more good with a first aid kit and a supply of sulfa powder, rather than with surgical instruments. He stated that he would be too busy to bother with us and that we would have to get along as best we could. Johnn's face froze up, and for a minute I thought Johnny was going to hit "Beartracks," which was utterly justified. Our love and respect for "Beartracks" is utterly nonexistent, the stupid jerk.

September 7, 1943—At sea

Very fine weather, and conditions are much like a pleasure cruise. We are allowed on deck after blackout, and it is lovely. We are moving through a very phosphorescent sea tonight, and it is quite a sight. There appeared to be hundreds of flashlights moving through the ship's wash. About noon today, we passed the Golite Islands, and about 5:00 P.M. we neared Bizerte, passing along the Cornish beaches in the outer harbor. We crossed the mouth of the Gulf of Tunis and sighted Cape Bon off our starboard bow about dusk. Moving very slowly, killing time.

4

September 8, 1943—At sea

Passed the western tip of Sicily this A.M. Sicily appears very rugged. Sighted several other convoys. Tomorrow is the day. We are slated to land about four or five hours after the initial assault, which occurs at 3:00 A.M. Sailed slowly up the Tyrrhenian Sea in a northeasterly direction all day. One air raid alert proved to be a B-24. All quiet otherwise. Just as we sat down tonight to dinner, it was announced over the speaker system that Italy had capitulated. There was much cheering and excited talk about the war being over and about going home! We are going ahead with the landing as planned. *The fact that we are going ashore with only one unbloodied, inexperienced American division, i.e., the thirty-sixth (Texas National Guard Division), did not worry us in the least. After all, we were anticipating that we would have little or no resistance from the Germans now that Italy had capitulated.*

September 9, 1943—Red Beach south of Sele River

D Day. This was a memorable day. At 3:30 A.M. the initial assault took place, but only with bitter fighting. No preliminary naval bombardment due to Italy's capitulation, and we found out the Germans were all set. The Yellow Beach at our southern flank was untenable for some time because of the 88 fire from the mountains back of the beach. From the ship we could hear the firing and see considerable smoke and dust along the land. Our ship lay to about twelve miles offshore. About 10:30 A.M. there was a bombing attack and from the deck of the ship I could see large geysers of water spouting from exploding bombs inshore. Enemy planes flew over us but no near bombings. It's funny how enemy planes seem to be always directly overhead, even though they really aren't. We climbed down cargo nets into landing craft about 2:30 P.M. and came ashore. This took about two hours. During this entire voyage, two cruisers lay about six or eight miles offshore and shelled the beach to the north of us. Their accuracy was amazing, and they started a large fire as well as an ammunition dump explosion. The flashes were visible from the guns, and after the sharp cracking sound of the supersonic shells passing overhead the bursts were visible. The firing and bursting concussions came seconds later. We ran up close to the shore and jumped into about knee-deep water. Johnny and I dumped our packs with the rest of the men and set out to locate the 602nd Clearing Station site, walking about two miles to the southwest corner of Paestum, where it was supposed to be located. *Paestum—this ancient Greek temple looked very fascinating to explore, but the exigencies of the situation overcame my archaeological curiosity.* There were a lot of tanks, guns, et cetera around, but not a lot doing at this time. A few dead bodies had been collected at various spots, but it didn't seem too bad. There was a cruiser lying offshore blasting the mountains just back of, us and we learned later that three 88s were there that had been shelling our landing zone off and on. We were blissfully ignorant of all of this. We wandered nonchalantly along and found out that our clearing station was located about one mile north of where we had landed, so we hiked back up, finally locating it, and found the other teams mostly there. Maj. James Sullivan of Milwaukee, Wisconsin, who was supposed to be "floating Reserve," had been landed before anyone else and had given first aid to a number of casualties. The clearing station was located in a tomato patch about 200 yards from the beach. It was just being set up. I saw an abdominal wound but had no equipment to work with, so we evacuated him. While Johnny and I were wandering about, a couple of Jerry fighter-bombers came in low over the beach and threw a hell of a scare into the boys we had left behind. The enlisted men and Capt. Joe Barrett, my anesthetist, had been left on the ship to come ashore with the equipment, but did not show up. Tonight, we all dug slit trenches and most of the boys are sleeping in them. However, the ground is about two inches of powdery dust, so some of us went down to the beach and salvaged three or four navy life preservers, carbon dioxide type, which make, when laid parallel, wonderful air mattresses. My two blankets over them and gas mask for a pillow make very satisfactory sleeping. Trogh and I slept out of foxholes but had to dive into them about 12:30 A.M. because of an air raid. The flak is quite heavy around us; the A.A. boys shoot at anything that flies. There have been numerous shootings at P-40s, Spitfires, and even, of all things, P-38s all afternoon and evening. The courses in airplane identification have certainly been wasted on these A.A. boys. One Messerschmidt 109 lies on the beach with its tail shot off, but I saw none of our planes being brought down in spite of being fired upon by our antiaircraft artillery.

September 10, 1943—602 Clearing Station, D + 1

Another rather rough day. This morning, Johnny, Trogh, George, and I went down to the beach to try to locate Joe Barret and his equipment. There was considerable activity going on on the beach, and we wandered along the water's edge. George and Trogh sat down to rest, and John and I went on down to Green Beach, where we unexpectedly encountered Frank Hall. Suddenly we heard some planes coming up the beach low from the south. These planes had square wing tips and I was thinking, *What are those P-51s doing so low over the beach?* when suddenly a column of water shot up about 300 yards down the beach and all hell broke loose with A.A. fire, bombs dropping and

SWITZERLAND

MAP I*

RIVA

L. COMO

L. GARDA

MAP XII

MILANO

PARMA

GENOA

CASTEL
FRANCA

BOLOGNA

APE

MAP
XI

MAP
X

FLORENCE

PISA

MAP IX

VOLTERRA

LIVORNO

PIOMBINO

MAP
VIII

NNINES

ORBITTELO

MAP
VII

CIVITAVECCHIA

ROME

TYRRHENIAN
SEA

MAP
VI

ANZIO

CASSINO

MAP
V

CASERTA

MAP
IV

AVELINO

MAP
III

NAPLES

SORRENTO

SALERNO

MAP
II

PAESTUM

*MAPS NOT TO SCALE

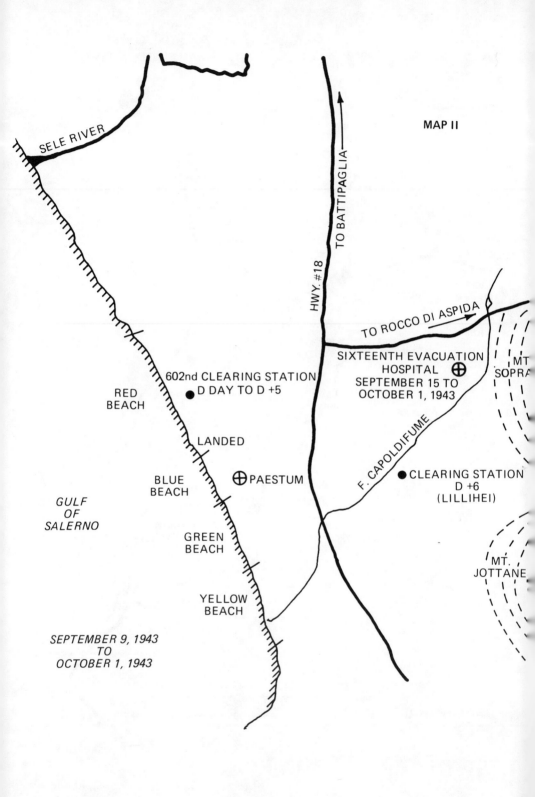

MAP II

SELE RIVER

TO BATTIPAGLIA

HWY. #18

TO ROCCO DI ASPIDA

602nd CLEARING STATION
D DAY TO D +5

SIXTEENTH EVACUATION
HOSPITAL
SEPTEMBER 15 TO
OCTOBER 1, 1943

MT
SOPRA

RED
BEACH

LANDED

BLUE
BEACH

⊕ PAESTUM

F. CAPOLDIFUME

● CLEARING STATION
D +6
(LILLIHEI)

GULF
OF
SALERNO

GREEN
BEACH

MT.
JOTTANE

YELLOW
BEACH

SEPTEMBER 9, 1943
TO
OCTOBER 1, 1943

strafing. There were no holes near us, so we dived into the sand alongside some bedrolls, feeling very naked and exposed. We were just at the bow of one LST (landing ship tank), and another LST lay perhaps fifty yards farther down the beach. A bomb hit in the water directly between the two, only 75 to 100 feet from us, completely demolishing an LCA (landing craft assault). There were only bits of flotsam left from this LCA. About the time we recovered our wits, the A.A. opened up again and we ran to the sand dunes, flopping in the foxholes in the middle of a morgue that contained about a dozen dead GIs. In the attack just finished, two soldiers about seventy-five yards down the beach from us had been hit by bomb fragments that went through their chests, killing them instantly. We decided that we had had enough of the beach and left, stopping by some delicious fig trees in a fig orchard on the way back and eating our bellies full. Later on, Joe Barrett showed up with quite a tale: He was just landing when the raid took place. A bomb sunk his LCA and dumped him into the drink. He lost all his personal effects but escaped uninjured. He managed to extricate himself and a boy who was caught in a blanket. Joe was later awarded the Silver Star for this rescue. He was certainly an exhausted forty-year-old man when he found us. Air raids at 11:30 A.M. and again at 6:00 P.M. These foxholes and this powdery ground certainly make one filthy, but it really doesn't matter much. Johnny Adams had a bad thigh case this afternoon, and I had my first surgical case in almost exactly a year tonight. What a case! A rifle bullet through the left arm, left chest, lung, diaphragm, spleen, large and small bowel, and ending up somewhere in the left retroperitoneal pelvic tissues, involving the nerves to the left leg. I had to repair the sucking wound of the diaphragm, do a splenectomy, repair the intestines, and do a transverse colostomy. This patient was a boy by the name of Brown from Anderson, South Carolina. He was mentioned in my Legion of Merit citation as the first case of major surgery done on the European mainland in World War II. Later on, at 1:15, we had on old Italian brought in who had a strangulating hernia and I did him. Joe is an excellent anesthetist, and Trogh is a very fine assistant; in fact, I wouldn't want a better one. He sees what you are trying to do without being told. The enlisted men really work, too, and I wouldn't have thought we would be able to do this extensive surgery we have done under these conditions. Another air raid at 11:00 P.M. The usual clusters of flares dropped. This flare dropping is pathognomonic of German bombers. Slept okay in the tomato field, but very dirty. Our enlisted men found us this evening, and we hope to get our equipment. That jerk Beartrack Palmer came roaring up in a cloud of dust in his jeep. He presented the very

9

picture of a dashing hero singlehandedly winning the war. Dust goggles, bandana kerchief as a dust mask, 45 automatic on one hip, canteen on the other, gas mask across his chest, and silver leaves gleaming brightly. He caught us all lying around in the shade, not knowing that most of us had worked the better part of the night. No one leaped to his feet to attention, all of which apparently infuriated him. He got redder in the face and started screaming for us to get busy digging foxholes to regulation depth, breadth, and length, specifying the exact A.R. dimensions. We told him, "Okay, we will dig them deeper." He went off fuming. No love is lost at all between us.

September 11, 1943—602 Clearing Station, D + 2

Usual air raids at 4:30 A.M. lasting about half an hour. I did a left colostomy for extensive rectal wounds this morning. Johnny Adams put up a long tale about men dying from lack of our equipment (partly true) and chiselled a "DUWK," which, incidentally, is a really wonderful amphibious vehicle. Anyhow, he talked a boy into bringing our equipment to the hospital. The boys set up the tents, and we are sleeping like gentlemen again, on cots under mosquito bars, except Lemmer, who clings to his foxhole and culvert. Last night Trogh and I dug us deluxe foxholes just at the edge of our tent with seats and everything in them. The usual raids at 10:00 P.M., 1:00 A.M., and 6:30 A.M., with more planes making these attacks. We saw a tragic sight today about noon. They have made a landing strip about a mile or two east of here and six Spits were circling for a landing when some crazy "trigger happy" A.A. outfit opened on them, and when he did, as usual, the rest of the A.A. boys started. One poor fellow in a Spit was directly hit with a shell in the fuselage. The flash of it was plainly visible. He seemed to regain control momentarily, but then went into a spin, crashing and burning. He was so low, he had no chance of bailing out. Another was hit and glided down, while a third had a big chunk of metal knocked out of it. Finally, when the damn fool A.A. boys quit firing only two of the six Spits came in for a landing.

The early morning (4:00 A.M.) air raid caught Trogh and me rather unclothed, and we practically froze before it was over. I, at least, had my shorts on, which Trogh did not. There he sat, shaking and shivering, his only clothing being a helmet. When the raid was over, he was sucking his hand and remarking he must have scratched it on a tent peg, diving into his foxhole. Nothing was heard of this scratch until the spring of 1945, when Trogh had his own team. It seems that at that time he was holding a wounded man for an X ray and a tiny foreign body showed on the X ray. No wound was found in this area

10

of the patient so Trogh's hand was x-rayed and a tiny foreign body seen. I recalled his "tent peg" scratch (made by a tiny piece of flak) and wrote him up for a purple heart, which was awarded to him.

September 12, 1945—604 Clearing Station, D + 3

What a day! Usual air raid at 4:30 A.M. I spent about half an hour or forty-five minutes in my foxhole but managed this time to draw on pants and shoes but no shirt. I practically froze. Many more casualties brought in last night; in fact, all tents are filled to overflowing. Made triage rounds with Johnny and found about thirty-six cases in need of early surgery. Sullivan did a major abdominal case this morning; Hoffrichter and Cunningham each did an acute appendix. My two abdominal cases are in fair shape, but postoperative care is woefully inadequate. Starting immediately after noon, all teams except Hall, who had a severe headache and acted as triage man, started working at four tables and worked straight through until supper, doing about twenty cases. After supper, C rations as usual, did the rest of the cases, finishing up about 11:30 P.M. Johnny and I were hungry so we went several hundred yards distant to the fig orchard we had located, climbed the trees, and ate delicious figs until we were stuffed. A brilliant moon made the finding of figs easy. I saw a P-51 shot down quite close by a Spit. It seems that these Spits were circling for a landing on their strip and this one lone P-51 entered this landing circle. The square wing tips fooled a Spit pilot, he thinking it was a Messerschmidt, and I could clearly see the tracers hitting the P-51; white smoke came out of the P-51. The P-51 pilot turned at once and bailed out, the plane crashing nearby and burning. Forty casualties evacuated at 5:00 P.M. to a ship, thank God, including my two abdominal cases. There is an extremely heavy barrage tonight north of us, and it sounds quite close. Varying reports reach us. They say there is considerable fluctuation of battle over the same ground. This afternoon Johnny and his team were doing a wound on the lower extremity under spinal anesthesia and I was just getting ready to start a scalp wound under local anesthesia when we became aware of a lot of shouting. Looking out of the surgical tent, we could see all these people running away from the beach. Soon some of our outfits started yelling, "Gas, Gas!" I thought like lightning and asked my patient, "Son, do you know where your gas mask is?" He said, "Yes, sir." Sweeping all drapes aside, I said, "Go get it." He left forthwith. I went over to Johnny's table; he looked at me, at the patient and at the anesthetist, George Donaghy, and said to the patient, "Son, I had better find you a gas mask." He began shucking gloves, gown, and surgical mask like crazy. Hoffrichter, his assistant, did the same.

11

George Donaghy waited a moment and said to the patient, "You just lie here; you'll be all right. I will be back in a minute." George and I dashed out, leaving the poor wounded devil there completely alone and paralyzed from his chest down. I have often wondered what his thoughts were. I sprinted for my equipment and came up with my gas mask bag. Pulling the mask out, I quickly put it on. A deep inspiration was completely futile; nothing came through. My mind raced as I pulled the mask off. I remembered that a spring clamp was applied to the hose from the canister to prevent water from entering the canister if I were thrown into the ocean. Removing the clamp, I reapplied the mask but I still couldn't breathe. I pulled it off again and feverishly examined it. This time, I found a waterproof tape closing off the intake of the canister! I could breath through it finally!! Soon word came back that all was a false alarm. A gas container had broken on the beach while it was being unloaded, and a lot of Negro quartermaster troops had panicked. I went back, found my patient, and finished the job; the local anesthesia was still very effective. Beartrack roared up again today. I had given him some thought and evolved a scheme in my mind to attack his obvious weakness, i.e., his lack of surgical knowledge. When he showed up, I went to greet him, saluted him, and said, "Oh, Colonel Palmer, I want to ask your advice. Will you come with me?" He looked puzzled but came. I took him into the postoperative tent and began going over cases, asking him what he would do, for example, in wounds of the colon, whether he would do a primary closure, a loop colostomy, a Mikulicz colostomy, or a proximal colostomy. He uh'd and ah'd and finally said, "I think you are doing things just right. I have got to get back to Headquarters right away," and he did. (Later: this was the last time Beartrack bothered us! I wonder whatever happened to him!)

September 13, 1943, D+4

The day started with the usual air raid at 4:30 A.M. or thereabouts. Johnny Adams had gone back to bed when things had quieted down and suddenly a large dud shell whistled overhead, everybody ducked, and Johnny rolled out of his cot all tangled with his bed covers and mosquito bar. It took him half an hour to get things straightened out again, cussing the whole time. They are evacuating our wounded and postoperative cases again after two days of no evacuation due to the fact that it was too dangerous for hospital ships to pull into shore. We were filled to overflowing, unable to give the wounded proper nursing care; no washing, no food except K rations, and no drinks except heavily chlorinated, brackish warm water. There are the usual air raids at mealtime, but no great damage done, apparently. The 602 Clearing Station has to move tonight, and we have to move in the A.M. There is a tremendous battle going on north and northeast of here only a few miles away. Casualties coming back say we have been pushed back about five miles and the front line is only about four or five miles away. *In retrospect, I am amazed at the unconcern of all of our people at the nearness of our battle lines. We weren't in the least worried. After reading about the war from various accounts, namely Mark Clark's* Calculated Risk, *Liddel Hart's* History of World War II *and others, I am appalled to learn that plans were being made to evacuate the beachhead. Another Dunkirk? This is another example of ignorance being bliss.* Tonight a big naval vessel or two were firing inland to the north and northeast of us. The clusters of nine shells could be seen arcing across the sky for a tremendous distance. The sequence observed was as follows: There was this huge flash of the big navy guns being fired. In a few seconds the clusters of nine shells began to heat up, from passing through the atmosphere, to a white hot heat. The shells seemed to float across the sky for an incredible distance, then descended and exploded. Only then was the sound of the firing from the shells and later the sound of the shells exploding heard. It must be pure hell to be on the receiving end of this barrage.

There is a cane brake and a small stream on the beach side of our tomato patch. Ever since the first night we have been hearing low talking and other stealthy sounds coming from this cane brake. Today, John and I, since we had little or no work, decide to see what was going on. We entered the cane brake by a small path and found twenty or twenty-five Negroes lying around. They all looked very frightened and big-eyed, and we asked them what was going on. They said they were scared to go on the beach, and I guess they were! They were hiding like animals in this thicket, which gave good concealment but no real cover. They were quartermaster troops supposed to be unloadiing supplies, and had been hiding since D day. Poor Lemmer, our shock man, is pitiful. He seems completely terrified whenever there is an air raid. He ducks into a small culvert draining the small stream mentioned above and even stays there for hours at a time. Unfortunately, the culvert is not high enough, so he sits in water all this time. The seat of his pants never dries out. We have started to call him "Wet Pants," but not to his face.

September 14, 1943, D + 5—Salerno Beachhead
6:30 A.M. struck tents. 9:30 A.M. ate breakfast, then went after a "bait" of figs. 10:30 broke out checkerboard and lost five games in rapid

succession to Trogh. 11:15 nasty air raids. They bombed a large cargo vessel five hundred yards from us loaded with gasoline. It burned fiercely all day, with ammo and gas drums exploding right along. 12:00 noon went to beach with Johnny and George to view burning ship. I know it would be safer to stay away but I always have to see what is going on. 1:30 P.M. a large number of Forty-fifth Division troops came into our area and fixed battle packs. Lemmer is very nervous that we will be strafed and bombed, but I am personally happy to see this good old Thunderbird insignia around us. 3:30 P.M. one of our enlisted men, Klempner, is quite ill with malarial chill. The mosquitoes are fierce around here, and chances are we will have it before too long, although Atabrine may keep it in check. 5:00 P.M. truck arrived to move us and we all piled on. Had gone perhaps a quarter of a mile when another air raid by low flying Messerschmidts occurred. Everyone dove off the truck and fell in the dust. Saw two of the bastards go down. George lost his cigarette lighter and fountain pen in the dust, and he was certainly a sight, pawing in the four-inch powdery dust with his face caked, clothes muddy from the dust and sweat and cussing a blue streak. He never did find his lost articles. 6:00 P.M. arrived at new bivouac area, which is about four miles inland and very slightly southeast of our clearing station site. Pitched tents and set up. George and Johnny started their gin rummy game when the moon came over the mountain, but there were too many mosquitoes for kibitzing. A Jerry plane had apparently jettisoned a large bomb during the last raid to get over the mountains, and the bomb had hit an engineering outfit 300 yards from our new site, blasting a huge crater, killing five and injuring many. The flak is vicious around here. A piece four inches long and one inch wide went through Captain Lilliheis's tent this afternoon. The burning ship blew up early this morning, but I didn't see it. No air raid last night. Incidentally, night before last, we saw a Beaufighter shoot a German bomber down in flames. It was quite a spectacle, but the only drawback was that the plane appeared to be coming directly at us. However, it went into a nose dive and missed us by a good margin.

September 15, 1943—Sixteenth Evacuation Hospital
At 7:35 A.M., a nasty air raid by low-flying M.E.'s occurred this time. Two were shot down, but they set fire to a Liberty ship carrying gasoline and an LST lying alongside the Liberty ship. The huge column of smoke shot up from the ships, mushrooming out at about 5,000 feet and forming a tremendous black umbrella overhead. I understand the ship sank in about two hours. From 9:00 to 10:30 A.M., dug flak-proof

foxholes, sweating profusely and requiring salt tablets. I then went over to a nearby stream, which was about nine feet deep and six feet wide and had crystal clear cold water, and I mean cold. Shaved, bathed, and did a bit of laundry and swam. 12:30 P.M. second air raid, maybe two or three of the raiders shot down. 1:00 P.M. borrowed Captain Denny's jeep and went up to look at the bomb crater. It was amazing. Twenty-five feet deep and fifty or sixty feet across, with huge chunks of earth hurled for hundreds of feet. No wonder it killed and injured so many in the engineering outfit. 1:30 P.M. Captain Lillihei, who later was to become professor of surgery at the University of Minnesota, told us we were moving to the Sixteenth Evacuation this afternoon. Lillihei invited us up to his tent and broke out a bottle of "Old Overholt," which sure was good and a fine gesture. Lillihei told me that he was going to ask for me and Johnny Adams when they needed surgical teams again. He is a swell gent, incidentally from Minneapolis. He is intensely interested in surgery and asked many questions. 3:00 P.M. loaded on trucks and stopped at the Ninety-fifth Evacuation Hospital, and who should be there but the boys from Sicily, including Black Robby, Hopkins, Hoffman, Shefts, Russell, Gumess, and others. The boys at the Ninety-fifth Evac are working very hard. 4:30 P.M. arrived at the Sixteenth Evacuation Hospital, which is located in a wheat field one mile east of railroad on the road to Rocca D'Aspide. They were just getting organized and set up, but the patients are piling in already. Set up our tents. Air raid during this, and a boy just across the road lying in a foxhole hit by flak in the chest died shortly after he was brought in.

7:00 P.M. Johnny and I went down the road about three-quarters of a mile to the stream I previously described. I bathed in a nice millrace. We examined a German tank Mark VI on the way, which seemed to have nothing much wrong with it. On the way up, we saw a number of wrecked German tanks, which were knocked out (sixteen of them) about noon on D day. During the past two days, waves of our B-26s and B-25s have been bombing the enemy northwest of us, and I shudder to think what would happen if they were doing the same to us. The ground rumbles and shakes even here. There is a battery of 155 Long Toms just back of the hospital and one about one-quarter mile down the road. They fired at intervals all night, the shells whistling overhead with quite a racket.

September 16, 1943—Sixteenth Evacuation Hospital

At 9:00 A.M. Johnny Adams and I went over to a quartermaster outfit, borrowed a truck, and went down to the Ninety-fifth Evac to recover our instruments. Other teams had borrowed them three or four days ago because they only had two sets. Saw some of our outfit. We got back about 10:00 A.M. and started working, all teams. Fifty casualties piled up, but they were mostly just debridements. We worked straight through until 1:00 A.M., then were relieved. I had two nasty burn cases, which took a long time, besides a lot of other stuff. No abdominal cases. Our boys are finally pushing the Jerries back, and the noise of battle is quite distant. Air raids at noon and 5:30 P.M. and a severe night raid at 10:00 P.M., but I slept well last night.

September 17, 1943—D + 8, Sixteenth Evac

It is strangely quiet around here. The artillery around us has moved out, and the air raids have practically stopped. Was supposed to be off today, but my team was called in last night and we worked until 12:00 midnight. The casualties are still quite numerous, but we are beginning to catch up a bit. This afternoon, Johnny, George Hoffrichter, and I went down to the nearby stream and took a bath in the subzero water. Or at least it felt like it. Very exhilarating afterwards, however. The Italians around here are a sorry lot, and why Mussolini ever felt the Italians could ever be "rulers" I don't know. Blackout begins early now, and there is little to do except to go to bed or sling the bull after 7:30 P.M.

September 18, 1943—D + 9, Sixteenth Evac

Tom Ballantine and Charlie Dowman came in today with the Ninety-fourth Evac. There are now four evac hospitals in the area. The Sixteenth, Ninety-third, Ninety-fourth, and Ninety-fifth. None will be particularly overworked now, I imagine. Did six cases today, the biggest one at 1:00 A.M., which no one else wanted to do. A fellow by the name of Lichtenstein had been hit in the right flank by an explosive bullet, and it really did explode, laying the side wide open, destroying all the flank muscles, exposing the peritoneum an area about eight-by-eight inches, but miraculously not injuring the kidney or ureter. The skin of the entire back was dissected off by the explosion. Worked all morning and afternoon. On the whole, our group has done very good work and, as far as I can see, are doing much better war surgery than the Sixteenth Evac boys. They don't seem to realize the underlying damage that is done to structures even though the skin lesion appears insignificant.

September 19, 1943—D + 10, Sixteenth Evac

Was supposed to be on duty all day, but there was absolutely nothing to do this morning so I went to church and even took communion. Worked this afternoon and tonight doing six cases. We got in a number of five- or six-day-old casualties who had been captured and recaptured. The Germans had given them no medical attention and wouldn't even give a Private Reed a drink of water for a day and a half. He stated he asked for water constantly; he had large wounds of both thighs and had bled considerably and was very thirsty. The funniest case I had was that of a Corporal Keefe who had a perforating bullet wound in the left forearm. It seems he and a buddy had found an Italian automatic rifle. They were artilleymen and were not on the battlefront but far behind the front. They decided to have a little fun and set up a two-man antiaircraft team. Keefe admitted he didn't know what planes were U.S. and what were Germans, but there were going to shoot at planes regardless. So they set up this rifle and, knowing nothing or little about its operation, got it all lined up. Keefe happened to walk in front of the gun just as his buddy fooled with something and promptly got shot through the forearm. Keefe stated, "My buddy wrapped a bandage around my arm and ran like hell in one direction while I ran like hell for the medics." Here was a two-man army with a 50 percent casualty rate!

September 20, 1943—D + 11, Sixteenth Evac

Not much doing today. Played Trogh gin rummy and checkers and lost somewhat. Worked this afternoon doing four cases, but none amounted to much. Distant air raid this morning, but I didn't bother to put on my helmet since the war had passed us by. There are lots of Italians being brought in, civilians and soldiers, with wounds of various sorts, mostly neglected. We treat all emergencies regardless of race, color or creed. The D + 12 convoy with the nurses is due in tomorrow but we have done pretty well without them. Scotty and Arnold (*T-5 Vernon A. Scott, Des Moines, Iowa, and T-4 Omar W. Arnold*) had been swell and worked like Trojans.

September 21, 1943, D + 12

The hospital is full, and no more patients are being admitted. There was not a great deal of work to do today and only two operating tents were running so we didn't start work until after supper because of lack of room. Had a run of orthopedic patients for a change. Saw some nurses for the first time today. They were the Eighth Evac nurses, and they are certainly needed around here for all postoperative care, which is terrible. We worked until midnight and pretty well cleaned things up. It is reported that a big offensive started this morning, and judging from the number of casualties admitted, I believe this is right.

17

Tonight, the flash of big-gun fire is seen to the northeast, followed much later by a distant rumble of explosions. Evidently the navy is shelling the peninsula between the Gulf of Salerno and the Gulf of Naples. Wish I would get some mail.

September 22, 1943, D+13

Well, the boys from the second wave (Madding, Jarvis, Hurt, Red Robertson, and others) arrived in the bay last night and debarked this morning. They all arrived here at the Sixteenth Evac together with the Eighth Evac (University of Virginia Unit). The Eighth was supposed to set up with us, but they all moved in within an hour to an adjacent field because of a violent argument between Colonel Bauchspies, the CO of the Sixteenth and the CO of the Eighth Evac. They set up pup tents over across the fence, including nurses' pup tents, all because of petty army rank and dignity. The Eighth lost every bit of their equipment when the freighter it was on was torpedoed a few miles out and sank. Their personal stuff was with them and they saved it, but everything else was lost. All the Eighth enlisted men set to work digging foxholes, which made us laugh. There hasn't been a raid in a week, and no one thinks of foxholes any more, except for reminiscences. Had a rather large surgical day, five cases including an abdominal case with a large infected subhepatic hematoma in a thirteen-year-old Italian boy hit twelve days ago. He will get well, I'm sure.

September 23, 1943—Sixteenth Evac, D + 14

The nurses of our team finally arrived today, on an LCI from Bizerte. They had quite an experience, having arrived in the Bay of Salerno on D+3 on a hospital ship. That night, their ship and four others pulled out about twenty miles and laid to. The ships had their lights on and were plainly marked with a large red cross. About 4:00 A.M., a German plane attacked them and got a hit admidship of the vessel carrying our nurses, killing twenty-three persons, including six British nursing sisters, a number of British doctors, and some of the crew. It was rather horrible in the respect that the British sisters were on the upper deck, the bomb explosion jammed their doors, and when they did try to get out of the portholes, their hips were too big and lower parts of their bodies were burned while the upper part hung out the portholes. None of the nurses of our outfit was hurt except for bruising, et cetera, and all were rescued by another hospital ship and taken back to Bizerte. All their bedding rolls, et cetera, were lost except for hand luggage. Each nurse was bringing several letters to team members, but unfortunately they had left them back at Headquarters in Bizerte.

18

September 24, 1943, D + 15

Everything has been so quiet, the war seems about over for our part at least. The only thing going on now are numerous P-40s, P-51s, and DC-3s overhead, and at night flashes from artillery can be seen to the north and northwest. Progress is very slow, but the Russians seem to be rolling against the Germans in Russia. Did five small cases today, and to occupy my time I played Trogh some gin rummy, being "Sneidermaned" two times and losing about eight bucks. Wish I would get some mail.

September 26, 1943—D + 17, Sixteenth Evac

Today seemed like Sunday at home, everything so quiet and peaceful and leisurely. The Ninety-fourth Evac has moved forward ten or twelve miles and is getting first crack at the casualties now. Had a chance to go with the British in a casualty clearing station, but turned it down because we weren't ready and couldn't get ready. Gordon Madding, a Mayo Clinic confrere, and Paul Kennedy went instead. The next time I get such an invitation, I am going just to see what it is like. The Sixteenth personnel got a lot of mail today, but none came for us. Joe Barrett and I got a weapons carrier and went down to the APO, but still no luck, damn it!

September 27, 1943, D + 18

Another quiet day. Very few new patients. Wrote up some reports and played gin rummy and checkers with Trogh, losing in the former, and in general did nothing much. Tonight, Johnny Adams broke out his five gallon can of 95 percent ethyl alcohol, got ahold of some lemon powder, and after dark we sat around—that is, Bill Edwards, Johnny Adams, George Donaghy, and I—and inbibed enough to get quite conversational, discussing at great length and with some heat the treatment of fractures of the forearm, war wounds, gas gangrene, et cetera. Needless to say, I slept well.

September 29, 1943, D + 20—Sixteenth Evac

What a hell of a night! About 7:30, Trogh and I were in the recreation tent playing checkers when the wind started to blow and a dash of rain hit the tent. We remembered that our tent was open, and I sprinted for it. The wind, by that time, was a screaming gale, coming off the Tyrrhenian Sea. It was raining furiously. We managed to get our flaps down, when it became apparent that our tent was going down unless something drastic was done. Trogh and I each got in a back corner, stepped on the tent flaps, and braced our backs around the corners. The pegs all pulled out, and we had to hold it up for about

19

our tent.

Sixteenth Evacuation Hospital leveled by sudden storm, September 28, 1943.

half an hour of real exertion. Finally the wind calmed a bit, but hail
and rain were still coming down. Joe relieved me in my corner, and I
went outside and tried to drive some stakes by the lightning flashes,
finally getting the corners anchored. I was trembling from overexertion
by then and naturally was soaked through and through, besides being
frozen. All around us, the lightning showed the devastation. Our tent
and Hall's and Hurt's tents were the only tents standing. Two of our
nurses small wall tents weathered it, and one of the Sixteenth Evac
officers' tents was still standing. Everything else there was leveled—all
the ward tents, the operating room tents, mess tents—everything was
down. Johnny Adams and his crew held up their tent until it all seemed
over, when Johnny went to back, found all the pegs out, and yelled for
help. Everyone dashed out to help. A gust of wind hit the tent, and
down she came. The hospital was demolished, but they did a swell job
of getting the patients evacuated by ambulances and trucks to some
warehouses and barns in the vicinity. This evacuation took only about
an hour. It was terrible for some of the seriously ill, but fortunately

20

no one was hurt further. Johnny got his tent back up right away. The nurses had no place to sleep, so six of them slept in our tent on Joe's, Trogh's, and my beds. We moved up to Johnny's tent with our bedrolls and slept on the floor. About 4:00 A.M. a lesser storm hit, which made it necessary to replace a lot more tent pegs, but no further tents came down. We had trenched our tent, fortunately, and it was quite dry inside. Today, there is a dreadful mess. Everything from Kotex to love letters is scattered all over the countryside. Believe me, we really fixed our own tent today so even a hurricane couldn't blow it down. Don't know whether the hospital will be set up again or not, but Colonel Bauchspies is a determined man. I can understand the fear of the ancient mariners' encountering a squall line such as this while at sea.

September 30, 1943—Sixteenth Evac, D + 21

We got news today that we were to move up with the Third Division Clearing Station "somewhere in the vicinity of Montemoreno." Be ready in two hours, so we got Arnold and Scott, packed, struck our tent, and then sat around all day waiting for transportation. After supper, word came that we would leave in the morning, so we had to unpack our bedrolls and sleep in Johnny's tent. Tonight we got some lemon powder and alcohol and got slightly ethylated. Personally, I will be glad to move on, for the work here is none at all. No mail yet.

October 1, 1943—Third Division Medical Clearing Station

(Ten miles west of Montemoreno) What a day. The trucks arrived about 8:00 A.M., so we got loaded, went to the Ninety-fifth Evac, to borrow instruments (I had given all my supplies to Gordon Madding), and started north. Saw considerable evidence of battle between the Sele River and Battipaglia. Tanks burned out, houses demolished, trees shot down, et cetera. Battipaglia was a shambles, having been bombed by the air corps. At the junction near Montecorvino, we ran into the Thirteenth Artillery Brigade convoy, and from there on the going was terrible. The Germans had systematically blown every bridge, and although they have been made passable by our engineers, the convoys are held up. It was a beautiful day so it wasn't so bad. Johnny, George, and Frank had come along for the ride, and about 4:00 P.M. they began to get worried for fear they would be AWOL. We went through Acerno, Montella, Prazzo, et cetera. Bridges had been blown out every couple of miles. In a pass between Acerno and Piazzo, there was terrific evidence of battle. Arrived at Montemoreno about dark and heard that the Third Division Clearing Station had gone on toward Avellino. The last ten miles took about three hours. Located the Third Division Clearing Station but were blocked by a tank, one of which had slid off the road and tied up traffic completely. I hiked about one mile to the Third Division Clearing Station and then came back in a borrowed command car. Tankers were having a hell of a time trying to build up the road so that they could proceed, not realizing that another road ran parallel to the one they were on about 100 yards away. While waiting, I reconnoitered and saw that the tanks could easily cross over to the parallel road, so I got the kid captain who was in charge of the tanks and showed him the situation. He surely was pleased and relieved and thanked me profusely. The tanks were rapidly cleared out then. Thus I helped, in a miniscule manner, the war effort. Had coffee when the truck arrived at the clearing station and went to bed.

October 2, 1943—Third Medical Battalion Clearing Station, Avellino
Today is my birthday, and it is rather a hectic one. We moved up to Avellino this morning in a convoy taking about three and one-half hours to come fifteen miles. It poured rain all the way. In the command car with me was Lieutenant Agnew and Captains Kane and Potelimos. We had a bottle of wine to keep us warm. On arrival, found that the clearing station was holding a mine casualty for me. This lad was very well blown up. I set up and started to work about 4:00 P.M. and worked straight through until 3:00 A.M. Did my first war nephrectomy.

Colonel Hugley, the division surgeon, came in about 2:00 P.M., and I had a nice talk with him. Told him from the looks of things that we could sure use another team and suggested Johnny Adams. He immediately put in a call for Johnny, requesting them up at once. Incidentally, Johnny, George, and Frank had caught a ride back on an ambulance last night, leaving about 11:00 P.M. The clearing station is set up in a military school similar, I presume, to VMI. It has been pretty well bombed by us, as has the rest of Avellino. Some of the buildings are very nice, however, quite usable. The officers in the clearing station are swell people. Captain Stewart is the CO; he is from Duluth and a swell gent.

October 3, 1943—Avellino, Third Medical Division Clearing Station
Worked a fair part of the day doing four cases. Johnny Adams rolled in about 5:00 P.M., much to our surprise. We put him to work at once. Johnny worked quite late, but we all got a good night's sleep.

October 4, 1943—Avellino
Worked hard all day. The first case was that of a little Italian boy hit in the belly, guts hanging out everywhere and jejunum severed in

three places. This was obviously a desperate case, but tried to save him anyhow. Finished the surgery, but made the mistake of trying to put him down to close him and it proved to much for him. The Italian civilians are sure taking a beating. Had two femoral artery ligations to do. A belly case followed. Then, helped Johnny on a couple of other cases. Finally got to bed at 5:00 A.M. The Third Division Clearing Station had movies last night and tonight in the gym, but I was called out both times to do cases.

October 5, 1943—Avellino
Slept until noon. This afternoon Johnny and I went strolling about town viewing the war damage. Stopped in and got some swell grapes from an Italian arbor. The owner's house had been demolished, but the owner was very friendly. Walked down to a bridge in the center of town that crossed the river. We had tried to bomb it out. The houses around each end of the bridge were a shambles and the odor of decaying bodies was terrible. There was a torso of a five- or six-year-old child lying near the bridge, both arms and legs blown off and the intestines hanging out. Must have been lying there at least a week. I can't imagine why the Italians don't bury their dead. It was quite a gruesome sight. Worked very light today, so went to bed early and got rested up. My anesthetist, poor Joe Barrett, is really taking a beating but is plenty game. No mail and not much prospects for any, I'm afraid.

October 6, 1943—Third Medical Battalion Clearing Station, Maddaloni, Italy
We got packed up this morning and waited until 2:00 P.M. for transportation to Maddaloni. While waiting, we went with Padre Martineau, the Third Division chaplain, and Trogh for a bellyful of those good grapes. When we returned, we found that the Fifty-sixth Evacuation Hospital was moving in to set up in this military school. I saw Charlie Bussey, a compatriot of mine from the Mayo Clinic, and talked with him a while. The ride up to Maddaloni was beautiful—very mountainous, but the Italian countryside is very pretty. There are lots of apples and oranges and quince and pomegranate trees. Also vineyards galore. Some of the town is pretty well shot up, but the natives greet us with enthusiasm and ardor. Set up in a former military hospital in Maddaloni. Had a critical chest wound when I got here, which I tackled shortly after arriving. The patient, a Sergeant Gaucos, from Nebraska, was hit by a bullet in the left upper anterior axillary line. The bullet traversed the left upper lobe, the mediastinum, the right upper and right lower lobes, and exited in the patient's right midaxilla, producing

23

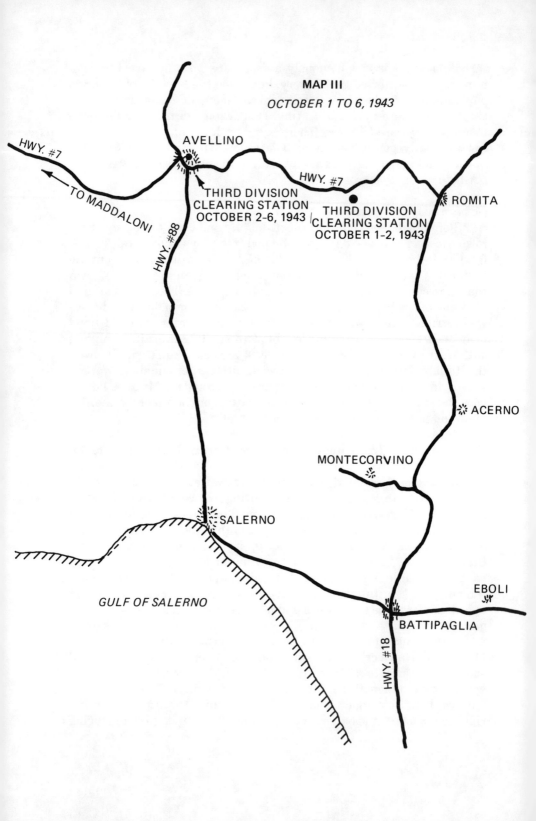

MAP III

OCTOBER 1 TO 6, 1943

HWY. #7

AVELLINO

TO MADDALONI

HWY. #7

ROMITA

THIRD DIVISION
CLEARING STATION
OCTOBER 2-6, 1943

THIRD DIVISION
CLEARING STATION
OCTOBER 1-2, 1943

HWY. #88

ACERNO

MONTECORVINO

SALERNO

GULF OF SALERNO

EBOLI

BATTIPAGLIA

HWY. #18

an exit wound you could have stuck your fist in. Boy, do we need endotracheal anesthesia with positive pressure anesthetic machines for this type of case! The army medical corps is still fighting World War I and is still using the same anesthesia equipment—namely, drop ether. Anyhow, still using the same anesthestic equipment, I went ahead and debrided the exit wound, tied off a bleeding intercostal, and evacuated a lot of blood clots from the patient's pleural cavity. I mobilized the latissimus dorsi and the pectoralis major on the right and closed the huge, sucking wound with these flaps. I believe I really helped the guy—in fact, never saw such marked improvement. He was moribund before the operation, but was begging for coffee half an hour after the operation.

October 7, 1943—Third Medical Division Clearing Station, Maddaloni, Italy

A very easy day today, only one fairly simple case. The casualties are light. Went to town both this morning and this afternoon. These people are very friendly and are anxious to please us. Went through the Convent of the Carmelites, and it was almost pathetic the way they skirt around trying to show us things. We gave them a couple of dollars, and one would have thought is was a fortune. Went to a number of shops, but the Germans had blown off the doors and taken what they wanted. We did pick up a few trinkets, and I got a very nice bedspread at a reasonable price. Tonight, some shells whistled over-head. We assumed that they were our 155 Long Toms firing from behind us, but we learned later that they were Jerry shells. They hit one truck about half a mile behind us, but did no other damage. Boy! it sure rains here every day, several times a day. However, we have a nice dry tent.

October 8, 1943—Same location

I chiseled a command car from Captain Stewart, and Trogh and I undertook the arduous journey back to Paestum, primarily to see if we had any mail. Secondary matters were the rest of my supplies and getting paid for August and September. We went via Highway 87, through Avellino and Salerno. The road through this country is very scenic. The Italians are a funny people. I have never seen one working yet, and all they do is collect along the main drag of their village and yell and wave when a United States vehicle passes. The kids scream for "Caramelli" and cigarettes. The Sixteenth Evac is a very dismal place now, and they are strictly a malarial hospital, doing no surgery. Well, the trip was a complete bust. Some of the boys had seen a few

MAP IV
OCTOBER 6, 1943
TO
JANUARY 4, 1944

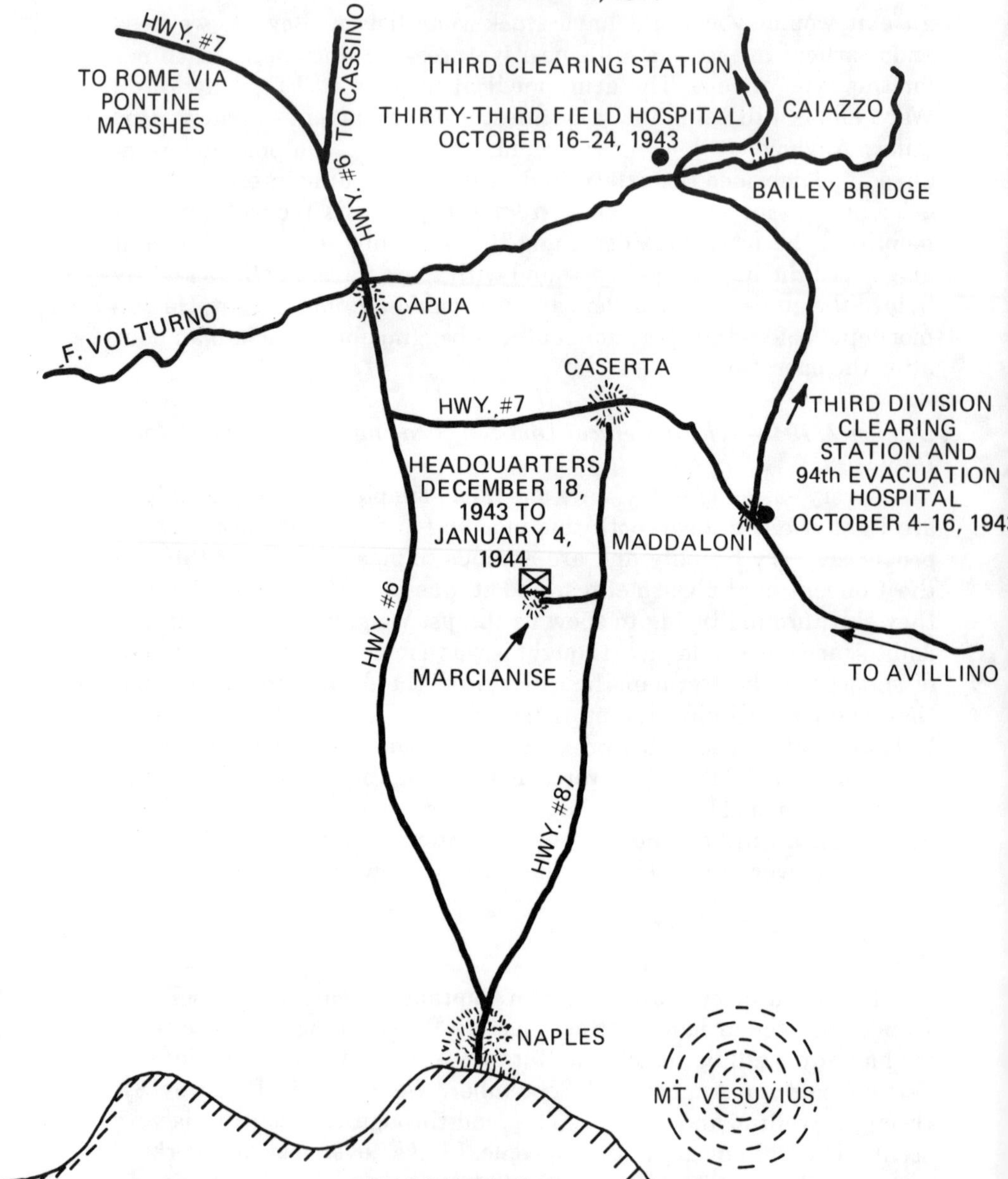

HWY. #7

TO ROME VIA
PONTINE
MARSHES

HWY. #6 TO CASSINO

THIRD CLEARING STATION

THIRTY-THIRD FIELD HOSPITAL
OCTOBER 16–24, 1943

CAIAZZO

BAILEY BRIDGE

F. VOLTURNO

CAPUA

CASERTA

HWY. #7

THIRD DIVISION
CLEARING
STATION AND
94th EVACUATION
HOSPITAL
OCTOBER 4–16, 1943

HEADQUARTERS
DECEMBER 18,
1943 TO
JANUARY 4,
1944

MADDALONI

HWY. #6

MARCIANISE

TO AVILLINO

HWY. #87

NAPLES

MT. VESUVIUS

BAY OF NAPLES

letters for us at the APO but these letters couldn't be found anywhere. Our instruments had gone to Naples with Frosty Lowry, and we couldn't locate a finance officer to get paid. So nothing was accomplished. The trip back was pretty grim, rain and darkness. I sure don't like to drive blacked out. The artillery was pounding away a good part of the night.

October 9, 1943—Maddaloni, Italy

A very quiet day with very few casualties. I had one Italian young woman three months pregnant with traumatic amputation of the leg and evidence of intra-abdominal injury. Johnny did the leg, and I opened her belly but found nothing. Very puzzling. Raining as usual. Took a nice, warm shower and got my laundry back. Tonight, Padre Martineau, Trogh, Hughes, Padalunas, Joe, and I broke out a little alcohol distillate and fruit juice. We ended up involved in a religious argument lasting two hours or more. Padre Martineau just naturally seems to attract the comments of other people, and I am afraid we got the padre quite confused religiously.

October 11, 1943—Maddaloni, Italy

Was awakened at 5:00 A.M. to see a fellow with a terrible wound of the left thigh and lower abdomen. Worked like the devil on him more or less all day. The Ninety-fourth Evacuation Hospital moved into this old military hospital this afternoon, and so I transferred all my patients down about 3:00 P.M., including the guy that I had been working on all day. Major Rife did a high thigh amputation on him later; he still came out of it, to the surprise of everyone. The condition and viability of these wounded boys really amazes me. Johnny, George, and Frank took off about noon for Paestum in Russell's jeep to see if they could locate the mail. They got back about 3:00 A.M. I had left word to be sure to wake me if they had any mail for me. Along about 2:00 A.M. German shells started hitting the vicinity, a loud whistle followed by a crashing explosion. These woke us up, naturally, but nothing to do, so I would go back to sleep between bursts. The shells came in about every fifteen minutes. No one seems to know where they are coming from. The shells sounded like 88s, not the large caliber stuff. About 3:00 A.M., George and Johnny got back with, thank God, three letters from Mary Will and one from my sister, Katherine. I naturally read them half a dozen times as quickly as I could. Boy, after six weeks of not having any mail, I really needed them.

October 12, 1943—Maddaloni

There is still a lot of mail somewhere for us, but we haven't been able to locate it. So this afternoon Trogh, Joe, and I borrowed Hopkins's jeep and went into Naples to see if the new base APO had it buried. The drive into Naples is beautiful, and Naples is in a marvelous setting, surrounded by mountains, a beautiful bay, and Mount Vesuvius overshadowing the whole with its constant plume of smoke. Naples itself is nothing much, as far as I can see. The war has damaged the city very little indeed, in spite of the fact that we had heard the Germans had almost destroyed it. The waterfront was banged about a bit, however. We saw Shorbe, Poole, Frosty Lowry, and Madding in Naples. The former three are with the Ninety-fourth Evac Hospital, and the latter at the British Eighth Casualty Clearing Station. We got back around 5:00 P.M. During the evening, since none of us had any possibility of work, we hung one on slightly. As usual, we gave the padre a workout, and he became so involved in the theological discussion that he ended up sitting there with a lighted cigarette in either hand, trying to decide which one should be smoked. A good night's sleep. I didn't even hear the barrage for the Volturno River crossing, which took place during the night.

October 13, 1943—Maddaloni

The river crossing (the Volturno) was successful yesterday, and the Ninety-fourth is flooded with casualties. Frankly, their system of getting the boys taken care of is horrible. They fill up one ward at a time, which overworks the teams having that ward while the others do practically nothing. Johnny and I pitched in and helped them a bit. The more I see of these war casualties, the more I am convinced that some of these guys that think war isn't bad should be made to stand around a clearing station or advanced hospital.

October 14, 1943—Maddaloni

Johnny and I worked pretty late last night clearing up some of the Ninety-fourth Evac stuff, which needed doing badly. Casualties are still quite heavy. Too bad this hospital can't get a better system going. These mine wounds are terrific! After we were all through, had a nightcap. Swingle, Russell, Hopkins, Brewer, and Dowman are attached to the Ninety-fourth.

October 15, 1943—Maddaloni

Well, we move forward again tomorrow, and I will be kind of glad to get away from the Ninety-fourth Evac because there is so much confusion. Colonel Sandzen and Maj. Charlie Rife are swell, but their system is all wrong. Johnny and Trogh borrowed a jeep and found two full sacks of second-class mail for us, but no first-class, damn it!

October 16, 1943—Three miles west of Piana De Caiazzo on the Volturno, Third Medical Battalion Clearing Station, Captain Stewart, CO

Well, here we are in tents out in a very nice grassy meadow with artillery all around us. Mosquitoes, yellow jackets, and various bugs and beetles are abundant also. We crossed a bridge the engineers had constructed that had been dive-bombed yesterday, but they had it in shape again. This was the first raid from Jerry in some time. It sure is good to see the A-36s, Spits, P-51s, and B-25s overhead almost all the time and not have to think where the nearest foxhole is. About thirty-six B-25s bombed a town the Germans hold five miles from here, and we saw them make their bombing run, pull out of it, and get surrounded by German A.A. fire. None was knocked down. The artillery is firing at intervals all around us, shelling over a mountain. The shells sound like a freight train going over a trestle. Tonight we had a little game; I lost eighteen dollars to the accompaniment of heavy shelling by our guns.

October 17, 1943—Third Division Clearing Station, same place on the Volturno

Today was a nice day, and fortunately very few casualties came in. In fact, nothing that couldn't be sent back. About 10:00 A.M., George and I strolled up to the battery of 105 Howitzers just across the road and watched them fire a few rounds. We were also shown how the guns work and are aimed, et cetera, as well as having the different fuses and shells explained. *Batteries of 105 Howitzers are usually located two to five miles behind the front line, which is a little close for our duties, in my opinion.* While watching this battery, we got a good view of German shells bursting on a hill a couple of miles away. Personally, I would hate to have been there. There was also a lot of white smoke streaks shooting up, but no one could explain what they were. I sure hope we get our mail soon.

October 18, 1943—Third Division Clearing Station, same place on the Volturno

Rain again today. Things are really very quiet, and we had absolutely nothing to do as far as cases are concerned. We spent the day getting straightened out, taking showers, et cetera. *Showers consist of the following: Obtain two empty one-gallon food cans from the mess. Fill one with water and put it on a Coleman stove to heat. Punch several holes in the bottom of the other can. Suspend this bucket from a tent pole or other object. Get naked, with soap and towel handy. Pour one-third of the heated water into the suspended can and generally get wet, lathering furiously. Refill the sprinkling can and rinse off. This is much superior to taking a sponge bath out of one's helmet.* Played poker tonight with Trogh, Stew, Mack, Johnny, George, and Don Nottingham and won my eighteen dollars back.

October 19, 1943—Same place on the Volturno, Third Division Clearing Station
The artillery has moved forward so progress is pretty good. Nothing doing today as far as emergencies were concerned. Played checkers and gin with Trogh and finally got to him in gin, Sneidermaning him twice. Trogh and I were playing checkers when Arnold wandered in and asked, "Captain, what's your middle initial?" Trogh said, "Why?" "Well," Arnold replied, "I see in the *Stars and Stripes* where a Capt. Trogler F. Adkins had a baby boy." Trogh had been very anxious to hear this, so he did lots of whooping and hollering. He broke out a bottle of Black and White Scotch he had been hoarding for this occasion, and we all had a few in honor of his new son. It sure was good!

October 20, 1943—Third Division Clearing Station, same place on the Volturno
I had a pretty good chest case today on an Italian girl of twenty, but I hate to have these Dagos around except under anesthetic. They are so blamed noisy that it gets on one's nerves. The nights are sure getting cold, and even the days are cool. I got my Primus stove rigged up, heated a bucket of water, and had a wonderful hot shower. Description of showers as noted above in italics. This Third Division outfit is really efficient and knows how to live in the field, and the chow is wonderful that they put out. Got three letters from my wife today and two others from my family. Boy, did I absorb them!

October 21, 1943—Third Division Clearing Station on the Volturno
What a day and a night! After fooling around all morning, Johnny and I decided to ask Stewart for transportation to Naples to see about getting some transportation for our teams. Stewart said okay and decided to go with us. So off we went. We visited the king's palace in Caserta, where Corps Headquarters is located, and you never saw such large rooms and so many oil paintings, statues, et cetera. It was more like an art museum than a house. Needless to say, we got a firm downward thumb on transportation, but it surely doesn't hurt to try. On to Naples then, and we spent a couple of hours wandering in the downtown section looking at things to buy. As a result, we purchased a bottle of mustard, a bag of hazelnuts, some clothing for the kids, and a bottle of Dago Red. Naples stores are only holes in the wall, and they

have the same line of cheap costume jewelry and cameos, the latter of which are produced locally in quantity from conch shells. We got back about dark and found a bad belly case had just come in. Stewart helped me, and just as we finished another case came in, so it was about 2:00 A.M. when we finished. We had terrible news, too! The Thirty-third Field Hospital had come in next to us, and we have to be transferred to it! Larry Shefts and his team showed up, also, to join the Thirty-third. This evening, we went over to talk with some field hospital people. They had some tents up and were unpacking some equipment. Great disorganization everywhere. They have come from Sicily and informed us that they could handle their own surgery! While we were there discussing the situation, the clearing station boys sent a casualty over: a boy shot through and through the jaw with tongue damaged and jaw hanging down on his neck. He would not and could not lie down and wrote (his only means of communication) that he couldn't breathe unless he sat up, which was absolutely correct. The CO of this platoon of the Thirty-third is a maxillofacial surgeon from St. Louis who said he would fix the boy up. Thinking that he would do it under local anesthesia and stabilize his jaw by wiring his teeth under local, we left. A couple of hours later, one of our men came in and told us that this boy had died. It seems that he had been given Pentothal anesthesia in a sitting position and was then laid on his back. He had no further respiration whatsoever. I was very upset over this entirely unnecessary death and wrote a report of it to Dr. Churchill. Very shortly, a directive from Fifth Army came out that field hospital personnel were not to do any surgery and that they were to limit their activities to housekeeping and administrative chores!

October 22, 1943—Thirty-third Field Hospital on the Volturno
I slept late and felt lousy all day—why, I don't know. We had a marvelous chicken dinner, our last official meal with the Third Division Clearing Station. We had everything, including frozen peaches captured from the Germans. I moved over to the Thirty-third Field Hospital afterwards. This evening, we had a dinner of Bully Beef and a can of C rations. Boy! is that ever a comedown from the Third Division Clearing Station mess.

October 24, 1943—One mile northwest of Dragoni, Thirty-third Field Hospital
Johnny and I bummed a ride up to the Sixth Corps Medical Supply depot so we could see what we could get. There was a very nice sergeant there who had a lot of respect for the Second Auxiliary surgical teams.

He promised to see what he could do for us in Naples in the way of certain supplies and tarpaulins for the floors. When we got back, I found a head and a belly case waiting, which were necessary to do without delay. When we finished, the Ninety-third Evac had rolled in and started to set up at the same site along the Volturno. *The Ninety-third Evac Hospital: This was the hospital in which the famous or infamous slapping incident by Gen. George Patton occurred in Sicily.* About 3:00 P.M. we packed up and left for our new location, passing along a narrow dirt road some fifteen miles north of Dragoni and on about one mile northwest to a new site in a field. We passed about everything, and the artillery is all around us. We are in this northern branch of the valley of the Volturno, and one can stand and see the front lines easily with shell bursts, small-arms fire, et cetera readily apparent. A jerry plane came over the front lines, and the whole range of mountains to the east of us was alive with flashes from antiaircraft. There is a battery of 105s directly behind us, and the noise of their firing is terrific. A small town on a hill five or six miles away is reported to be about to fall into our hands. The Thirty-third Field Hospital is doing a bit better at setting up, and the chow is getting somewhat better, too. After supper, the Jerry artillery started shelling a concentration of quartermaster and service troops about two miles behind us. We got about a dozen or so casualties from this. One could hear the shells whistling overhead easily. As a result, all of us worked all night before we got things cleaned up. Ordinarily we could have done these cases in four to five hours, but as it was, we worked from 7:00 P.M. until 7:00 A.M. A lot of corrections and reorganizations in surgery were discussed with the CO of the Thirty-third Field Hospital during the night.

October 25, 1943—Monday—Near Dragoni, Italy, Thirty-third Field Hospital

I slept until noon. Two batteries of 155 Long Toms moved in directly back of us and threw shells over our heads steadily. What a racket! When they fire, the tents flap, lights jump, your clothes flutter, and sleep is difficult. The report is followed by the sound of a freight train going through a tunnel. Someone sure screwed up in placing either the artillery or the hospital, believe me. Had a number of cases but was able to evacuate most of them except for some severe chest cases, which Larry Shefts did. Oxygen is certainly a hell of a problem, as well as Levin tubing, intestinal sutures, and other stuff we desperately need day after day. I would like to have some of those bastards back in the surgeon general's office in the United States over here with chest and belly wounds! They would certainly change their notions about what the Tables of Basic Equipment say are needed and what we should or shouldn't have. We have often talked about the need of sending some of us back who have had bad experiences to get the supply problems straightened out. There is so much junk sent that is never used and lifesaving things such as anesthetic machines, endotracheal tubes, Levin tubes, intestinal sutures, small hemostats, blood vessel sutures, et cetera are all absent. To demonstrate the gross futility of whoever made out our Tables of Basic Equipment, we have dozens of Miller-Abbott tubes in our medical chests, but not one Levin tube. As far as I know, no one has ever needed the Miller-Abbott tubes, but we need Levin tubes in practically every belly case. So we cut off about ten feet of the Miller-Abbott tube and the balloon and then used the business end of the Miller-Abbott tube as three to four feet of Levin tube. These tubes have such small diameter that they are quite ineffective, particularly when the casualty's stomach is full of recently ingested food—which is usually the case, it seems. We do have enough glass tubing and rubber tubing to contrive our own Wagensteen suctions from three intravenous bottles. These work quite well. Also, we need suction machines desperately. Surely the Army Medical Supply should know what it needs after a year of battle casualties and could have done something about it by now! I don't like the army, particularly for this reason.

October 26, 1943—Near Dragoni, Italy, Thirty-third Field Hospital
Was doing a belly case this morning when the lights went out and had to proceed with flashlights. Naturally, this outfit's emergency lights have no batteries in them. Then a bit later on, one of the Long Toms had a very short burst overhead and sprayed fragments around, with holes suddenly appearing in the tents. I noticed it, but when I'm working such things bother me very little. Hear that Colonel McCarthy caught hell from a two-star general for bringing us practically in the front lines. We got a bag of mail today in which I had seven V-mails. The letters had been soaked somewhere, but it sure was nice to get them even though they were partly illegible.

October 27, 1943—Thirty-third Field Hospital, near Dragoni
It rained all morning and flooded this outfit completely. The operating room had rivulets running through it, which left slimy mud underfoot, making walking a very ticklish thing indeed! Worked all afternoon on a lieutenant who had the worst shot-up gut I have yet encountered. I still don't know how he lived to get here, much less how he survived

all we had to do in patching him up. I know he doesn't have much of a chance to live, but I have been so surprised by what these boys can stand so that as long as the heart keeps beating, I will keep working. I had to throw the surgical textbook at him: gastric resection, bowel resection, et cetera. Boy! if these cases don't give one gray hair, nothing will. Oh! for a nice simple appendix or gallbladder once more! Played poker tonight in Stew's tent for a little relaxation and got my pocketbook relaxed. Our nurses, Francis Mosher and Ruth Hindman, finally caught up with us, arriving last night and being promptly put to work. They are going to find this lack of gadding about up here hard to take, no doubt.

October 28, 1943—Thirty-third Field Hospital, near Dragoni
The artillery has been pulling forward, thank heavens. This afternoon a single Jerry plane came helling over the mountain. Everybody opened up but nothing much happened. We got the football out and played a bit of kick this P.M. Went to a movie at the Third Medics tonight, something called *Escape Me Never*. Pretty good. A Colonel Freeman and Captain Kitchen (from Wake Forest) visited us today, and we gave them a few aperitifs of orange juice and ethyl alcohol, which they seemed to appreciate a great deal. Then we took them over to Stewart's outfit for lunch. Kitchen, Trogh, and Joe spent about three hours with "What happened to so and so?," "Do you know?," et cetera.

October 29, 1943—Thirty-third Field Hospital, near Dragoni
Lost a tough case early morning. We could have saved this boy except for a number of tough breaks and lack of equipment. His vomiting and aspiration of vomitus proved to be the deciding factor. This afternoon a number of Jerry dive-bombers came over, diving out of a cloud, and, boy, they really were moving! The ack-ack was shooting about one-half mile behind them. They bombed the artillery about five miles up the valley and caused quite a number of casualties among the A.A. boys and the artillerymen. We got in four or five of them: one with a terrific head wound, another with a huge hole in his chest, another with a leg blown off, and still another with left arm off above the elbow and right hand shattered. If the Germans can do this sort of thing with the few planes they have, I sure would hate to have our air force after us. We must send over twenty planes to their one. It rains every day, and this site has the slipperiest mud I have ever encountered. Ice is not as slippery.

October 30, 1943—Thirty-third Field Hospital, near Dragoni
Not too busy today. One belly case, which I let Captain Snatic, the

34

CO of the First Platoon, do with my assistance. He has had some training but hadn't done too much big surgery, obviously. Our nurses are quite bored with this life already, not enough nightlife. Maj. Howard Snyder, consultant from the surgeon's office, has been visiting us, and he went over our cases. He seemed quite pleased with the way we were handling things and wanted to take some pictures of my two colostomies but there was not enough light.

October 31, 1943—Thirty-third Field Hospital, near Dragoni
Worked rather late this P.M. Lieutenant Blackman from the Third Medics had been called in to inspect meat for the division, so he chiseled eight pounds of steak and we fried it in Stew's tent. Man, were those steak sandwiches delicious! First steak I have had in about two months. Captain Doud, one of our assistant surgeons, went to Caserta yesterday and on the way picked up an Italian who was dressed in United States uniform and carrying a German rifle. Doud got to wondering what to do with him and what he was, so he saw the provost marshall and G-2 in Caserta, who said the man was to be made a prisoner and put him in Doud's custody. Of course, the prisoner had the only weapon, so it was right embarrassing. Finally, Doud, after about three hours, got an M.P. lieutenant to take this man and breathed a sigh of relief. Got thirteen wonderful letters this P.M. Boy, did I ever need these letters.

November 2, 1943—Thirty-third Field Hospital, one mile west of Riardo
We moved up to a spot one mile west of Riardo this morning and sat around watching the struggles of this outfit getting set up. Soon after we arrived, about fifteen Jerry dive-bombers came over us, peeled off, and bombed the road up the valley about five miles north of us. And they brought a couple of boys of ours in about an hour later and I picked the biggest slug of bomb fragment out from under one of the boy's scapula that I have ever seen. Must have weighed a quarter of a pound. Our equipment arrived late this P.M., and we set it up in no time at all. We stole a tarp for our floor, which was a great help.

November 3, 1943—Near Riardo, Italy, Thirty-third Field Hospital
Got all cleaned up today and sent my laundry out to one of the local Dagos. One always takes a chance doing this, but I refuse to do laundry. The physical layout of this hospital is swell, and everyone is quite impressed. I believe Captain Snatic designed it, and it sure is a help as far as moving patients about and still maintaining a blackout. The design is based on a pyramidal tent in the center, to which on each side a ward tent is connected. Thus a cross is effected, one limb of which being the shock tent, another wing the operating tent and

supplies, and the other two wings postoperative wards. This permits free passage to all the areas without having to struggle through black-out curtains et cetera. Worked all afternoon until 1:00 A.M., and it was freezing cold tonight. Stoves have arrived and are to be put up tomorrow. These poor patients have enough to undergo without having intestines exposed to forty degree temperatures. Steam vapor rises constantly from the operative site in belly cases.

November 4, 1943—Thirty-third Field Hospital, near Riardo
Our mail is finally catching up with us, thank heavens. It is the biggest morale booster, at least for me, that I know of. It sure is cold at night now. We got a Sibley stove set up in our tent, which warms up in a hurry but dies down just as rapidly.

November 6, 1943—Near Riardo, Thirty-third Field Hospital
Our little Sibley wood-burning stove is wonderful, and our tent is real homey now. Had a case of abdominal gas gangrene at 5:30 A.M. Johnny and I did one of those horrible mine cases this afternoon, which also had gas infection of the thigh. Last night, Johnny had a buttocks wound that had a gas infection. There are too many of these gas infections recently; apparently the soil in this part of Italy has been fertilized for millennia with human and animal feces so that the soil is a veritable culture of gas gangrene bacteria. Got a lot of fairly recent letters from my wife with photos of the kids. I feel good.

Last night Johnny and I were informed that we would be attached to the Third Division Clearing Station until the Eleventh Field Hospital comes up. So this A.M. we moved up about eight miles to a meadow about one mile south of Presenzano, a hillside town that we were to view for the next two months. Mount Rotundo is on our right, and Mount Maggiori is on our left.

There is a dim situation here. We are completely surrounded by artillery, mostly British 5.5 pounders. Our A-36s are really giving them hell today, relays of twelve of them going over us to about six or eight miles up the valley to the Mignano Gap. We can plainly see them peel off in absolutely vertical diving for several thousand feet, then pull out and head back for us. *A-36 planes are P-51 fighters, equipped with diving slots on their wings to slow their speed when they dive-bomb vertically.* We are nicely set up, with tarp floor and stove. The Jerries blew down a lot of trees for roadblocks near us, and these make swell firewood for our Sibley stoves. Tonight the artillery is really laying down a barrage. Flashes everywhere in a continuous roar, quite loud bangs when the adjacent batteries turn loose.

November 7, 1943—Third Medical Clearing Station, near Presenzano, Italy

The day started off quite briskly. We had just finished breakfast and were watching a bunch of our A-36s going up to give the Jerries a dose of bombs when a flight of thirty-six of our B-26 bombers went overhead. Suddenly, under them appeared fourteen planes coming toward us from the north at a terrific speed. I edged over toward the ditch, and when I saw them start their dive, I dived also, but stuck my head up to watch what happened. They dived on a repaired bridge about two miles south of us, and two of them came up the road like a bat out of hell, strafing the road. Meanwhile, our A.A. boys shot madly behind them. They passed over the road about seventy-five yards from us, and their black crosses and flashing guns were very clearly visible. The rest of the fourteen scattered. The two strafing planes hit an oil truck about 200 yards up the road, and the gas cans exploded for about two hours. I went up and got some pictures of it. One of the boys from the truck was brought in with a slug in his thigh. About half an hour after the Jerry raid, six of our A-36s came over, apparently to see what was causing the huge black column of smoke from the burning truck. All the A.A. boys opened up on them in spite of violent waggling of wings and yellow stripes of the wings. Fortunately, none was shot down, as far as I could see.

We got another fellow in with a bullet wound through his chest as a result of the strafing attack, and we heard that a Major O'Neal, a medical officer, was taken to our outfit at the Thirty-third Field Hospital, with a piece of ack-ack in his brain. He died soon after. He was apparently with either the Thirty-eighth or the Ninety-fourth Evac about six miles down the road from us. Johnny and I went over to the Limeys' guns, and they showed us all about their 5.5's. Even said we could shoot them when they were firing. This afternoon it rained hard and we found that our tent was in a poor spot for drainage. The Thirty-third Field Hospital platoon moved up with us this P.M., and we are to be reattached to them. Oh, me!

November 8, 1943—Third Division Clearing Station, near Presenzano, Italy

This afternoon Johnny and I went up to the British 5.5 battery and saw the captain in command, a young chap, very pleasant. He invited us to fire the next salvo, so we took the lanyard in our hands expectantly. Soon the order came over the squawk box: "Prepare to fire," then "Fire!" I yanked my lanyard like hell, but nothing happened. The three other guns roared off in unison but mine remained quite

Strafing result, Third Division Clearing Station, south of Prezenzano, November 7, 1943.

docile. All the gun crew looked very surprised and upset. Naturally I thought, *Now what have I done wrong?* In a moment the captain said, "Wait a minute!" and opened up the percussion cap chamber, finding it quite empty. I guess the guy supposed to put in the percussion cap was so intrigued with our visit that he completely forgot to put the cap in. Anyhow, the captain quickly put a cap in, stepped back, and told me to pull. I yanked the lanyard again, with a satisfying result. The gun bellowed, jumped back, and sent a long shell on its way. I am reasonably sure that I must have killed a couple of Germans, because no one ever shoots except in salvos and the Jerries know it. They duck in their foxholes and dugouts for the salvo and know that they have time to emerge and enjoy life between salvos. Imagine their consternation and anger when a lone round descends on them about a minute late! Obviously this is not cricket and is most unsportsmanlike!

Frank Hall was taking a picture of the gun firing when two Jerries appeared overhead apparently on a reconnaissance mission. Our ack-ack was quite futile, as usual, and as the planes were overhead when the battery fired, they no doubt got excellent photographs. A little counterbattery fire to us seems probable. We were called out about 3:00 A.M. to see a case, and while I was checking him out, four more belly cases came in. Larry Shefts did one of them, a combined chest and belly wound, while I did the other. We sent the three in best shape down to the Thirty-eighth Evac about five miles south of us. Got to bed about dawn and immediately had the artillery open up all about us, which makes sleeping difficult, to say the least. Joe Barrett hung a slight one on last night, and it was certainly funny trying to get him up and moving this morning.

November 9, 1943—Thirty-third Field Hospital, near Presenzano
Tried to sleep until noon, but because of the artillery, flies, and Trogh stoking the fire to 100 degrees in the tent, gave it up as a bad job. Jerry planes came over about 9:00 and further disturbed us. After lunch, we struck our tent and moved a couple of hundred yards to the Thirty-third Field Hospital setup. Our being attached to the Third Division Clearing Station was a little premature, and we are back with the Thirty-third. About the time we got our tents up, patients started rolling in, and I worked until 5:00 A.M. Had to send two belly cases back, but they were in pretty good shape. One of my abdominal cases, a nice young lieutenant, died suddenly of pulmonary embolism today. I proved it at postmortem.

November 10, 1943—Thirty-third Field Hospital, near Presenzano
Did a very extensive case this evening. The infantry is meeting plenty of trouble, and artillery has been firing on the same targets for three days, according to the British lads around us. Twenty of these British boys came in last night as blood donors, and we sure used them. *From D day on September 9 until sometime in late December, all blood for transfusions was obtained from volunteers among the nearby service groups or the battalion of infantry in reserve. About twenty or twenty-five such volunteers showed up almost daily in our receiving tent. We would check their dog tags to see if they were type O, and, as needed, draw the blood into vaccuum transfusion bottles. No further typing and no cross matching whatsoever was done. Doubtless a few cases of renal failure resulted, but the lives saved by these blood transfusions numbered in the hundreds.* A Mr. Raymond, a *Saturday Evening Post* correspondent, is nosing around getting a story on the forward medical care of the army in Italy. Had a nice talk with him.

November 11, 1943—Thirty-third Field Hospital, near Presenzano
Today is Armistice Day, but there was no armistice for us here.

German planes came over a couple of times this morning, but they worked over mostly on the front lines. They must have twenty or twenty-four big artillery pieces, most 155 Long Toms, within a few hundred yards of us, and they fire intermittently all day and night. It is getting on some people's nerves somewhat, and I jump a bit myself at times.

November 12, 1943—Thirty-third Field Hospital, near Presenzano

Jerry lobbed a few shells over us last night, but no damage was done that I know of. Our artillery blasts away day and night, and the detonations of the guns and the roar of the shells tearing through the air are really something to hear. Did two cases this afternoon. One died on the table, fortunately. The poor kid had abdominal gas gangrene five hours after he was injured. The only reason I operated was because I had to make sure. This was the second straight case of abdominal gas gangrene that I have had today. It is really awfully discouraging. Mr. Raymond reported on this case of abdominal gas gangrene in his article in the *Saturday Evening Post* of January 1, 1944. Sully (Maj. James Sullivan of Milwaukee, Wisconsin) and his team rolled in about the time I was finishing the last case. I gladly arranged for him to take over. Two belly cases came in, and he worked until 4:00 A.M. Tonight, Johnny, Joe, and I decide to hang a slight one on with "Yocky-Docky", which we did. Joe really got looped, and neither he nor I heard the nightly barrage nor the Jerry 88s that whizzed over us during the night, although Trogh tried to arouse us.

Yocky-Docky requires elucidation! One of the truly magnificent accomplishments of the medical department of the United States Army was the inclusion in the Table of Supplies of a five-gallon drum of 95 percent ethyl alcohol, for sterilizing purposes. I firmly believe that this item was a hangover from World War I. Anyhow, each team was allotted one such drum. It soon became apparent that it was totally unsafe to leave this item with our other equipment, and to safeguard it, each team's senior officer had it under his direct care at all times, parking it under his cot religiously when set up for work and having it moved under his personal inspection when moving. It became apparent at once that this fine, clean, liquid had great value, when properly diluted and flavored, in relieving tensions and in making for splendid fellowship and conversation in idle moments. Also, hospitality to visitors was greatly enhanced by this wonderful substance. Various experiments were performed to determine the best ingredients, but finally the following standard recipe became available because of its quickness and ease of accomplishment. I do not know who coined the term "Yocky-

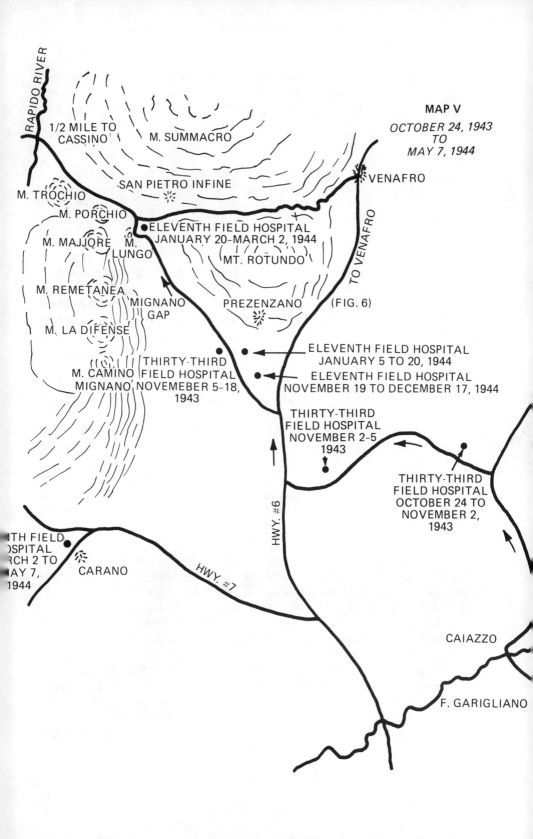

RAPIDO RIVER

1/2 MILE TO CASSINO

M. SUMMACRO

MAP V
*OCTOBER 24, 1943
TO
MAY 7, 1944*

SAN PIETRO INFINE

VENAFRO

M. TROCHIO

M. PORCHIO

ELEVENTH FIELD HOSPITAL
JANUARY 20–MARCH 2, 1944

M. MAJJORE

M. LUNGO

MT. ROTUNDO

TO VENAFRO

M. REMETANEA

MIGNANO GAP

PREZENZANO

(FIG. 6)

M. LA DIFENSE

THIRTY-THIRD
FIELD HOSPITAL
M. CAMINO NOVEMEBER 5–18,
MIGNANO 1943

ELEVENTH FIELD HOSPITAL
JANUARY 5 TO 20, 1944

ELEVENTH FIELD HOSPITAL
NOVEMBER 19 TO DECEMBER 17, 1944

THIRTY-THIRD
FIELD HOSPITAL
NOVEMBER 2–5
1943

THIRTY-THIRD
FIELD HOSPITAL
OCTOBER 24 TO
NOVEMBER 2,
1943

HWY. #6

ITH FIELD
OSPITAL
RCH 2 TO
AY 7,
1944

CARANO

HWY. #7

CAIAZZO

F. GARIGLIANO

Docky," but it must have originated among the teams of the Second Auxiliary Surgical Group and has become almost universally known by this name at this time. A standard prescription for Yocky-Docky is as follows:

Rx: 1 canteen cup, GI issue
  1/3 canteen cup of 95 percent ethyl alcohol, GI issue
  1/3 canteen cup of chlorinated water, GI issue
  1 package of lemon powder, a constant ingredient of K rations
  2 lumps of sugar, found in the K rations

Sig: *Misce*

One always kept a supply of lemon powder and lump sugar in a box, donating the rest to the poor starving Italians. With the mixture properly prepared and under candlelight, the people assembled would sit in a circle and pass the cup in a clockwise direction. Refills were prepared by the host as needed. Sanitation was quite well preserved by the alcohol, and I know of no case of disease that was recorded arising from the communal cup. This concoction was called Yocky-Docky and was one of the famed and brilliant evolvements of World War II. A careful objective study of the effects of this delightful cocktail was made by me, and some observations I recorded: (1) No headache, hangover, or other deleterious effects are ever noted; (2) conversation, debate and fellowship was sparkling and lively; (3) one felt no particular sensation of intoxication, no matter how long the session lasted, until (4) one tried to get to his feet, when it became apparent that the motor function of the lower extremities was quite unstable and uncoordinated, and (5) one slept soundly after imbibing, awakening with a clear and alert mind.

November 13, 1943—Thirty-third Field Hospital, near Presenzano
   Went down to the Thirty-third Field Headquarters for a meeting regarding records et cetera today. We passed our two previous locations and then went on to Dragoni over the Volturno and a couple of miles beyond. The war seems practically over back there, but it sure isn't over up here. Everything has been here as it was one week ago, except they have moved in a lot more artillery around us. The trouble is in Mount Maggiore, which extends on our northwest from the Volturno River to the Garaglioni. This is made up of four peaks, which are called from south to north Mount Camino, Mount LaDifensa, Mount Remetania, and Mount Maggiore; these mountains block our way to Cassino. The Jerries are really dug in on them. We can watch our shells

bursting on the mountains, especially at night. They have been trying to burn the Jerries out with phosphorus shells, which are quite impressive bursting on top of a mountain, throwing up a fountain of flaming smoke. We saw Red Robby, Bill Edwards, Jarvis, and Hoffman at the Thirty-third Headquarters. This promises to be a noisy night.

November 14, 1943—Thirty-third Field Hospital, near Presenzano
Last night was pretty rough. About 3:30 A.M., Jerry shells started bursting in the vicinity. The shriek of those shells sound like they are within three feet of you, and if you aren't scared it's because you are ignorant or a damn fool. One hit quite close, fragments raining about, and several ripping holes in the tents. I was flat on the ground when this shell landed, and then Joe, Trogh, and I got dressed and went down behind the bank of a nearby stream, staying there from about 3:45 A.M. to 4:40 A.M. No more shells dropped in, so we came out and went back to sleep on the floor. Captain Snatic got the nurses up at 3:30 A.M. and sent them back to the Thirty-eighth Evac. Fortunately, no casualties came in during the night and none today. Trogh, Johnny, Hoffrichter, and I spent the afternoon digging nice big foxholes in our tents. We placed our bedrolls in them, and I plan to sleep an unworried sleep tonight. *Probably the most welcome and satisfying objects in my military career were the good old dirt foxholes. Most shells are designed to explode on contact, spreading a sheet of shell fragments for a hundred yards or so ahead of the explosion. These fragments are what kill people. The foxhole, even though it is only two or three inches below the ground level, provides immunity from these shell fragments. I always figured that if one got a direct hit in one's foxhole, one wouldn't know what hit him anyhow. When shells started dropping in, the poor infantry guys in our postoperative wards often expressed a wish to be back in the safety of their front line foxholes.* It rained all afternoon and is raining again tonight. I slept swell last night in my shell-proof foxhole.

November 15, 1943—Thirty-third Field Hospital
I wasn't awakened last night, until 6:30 A.M., when a veritable cloudburst came down. I got up and went out to inspect the drainage system and make minor adjustments. Everything was working well. After breakfast, got my patients in order and was planning to go back to bed when word came over that Johnny Adams and I were to go out with the Third Division medics for a "rest." We began to get organized and waited until 3:30 P.M. for the truck to come back. It never showed up, so we borrowed a truck and weapons carrier, struck our tents in a downpour, and took off at about 4:30 P.M. for the designated spot the

43

other side of Petramelaria. We couldn't find the outfit. We stopped an ambulance, which contained Jackson, who was also lost. It was dark and raining by then, so we crept along under blackout and kept asking where the Third Division Clearing Station was. Finally found it five miles back from the spot that was designated on the map. They were in an awful shape. Mud knee-deep everywhere, and the place only half set up. They did have some hot coffee and Vienna sausages, which helped a lot. We all slept in their admitting tent, all being somewhat cold and damp.

November 16, 1943—Third Medical Battalion, near Riardo

Orders came through for us to rejoin the Thirty-third Field Hospital again from Col. "Huddlefuddle" Huddleston, Second Corps surgeon. These were written orders, incidentally, the first we have ever had. Our truck was stuck in the mud, and after a couple of hours, a wrecker pulled us out. Colonel McCarty, the Third Division surgeon, invited us in for a slug of bourbon, assuring us that he would do everything he could to get us back. The bourbon was swell, but I don't have much hope of getting back with the Third Division again. The Thirty-sixth Division is replacing the Third Division in the line, and the trip back was very tedious because of the continuous convoy. We got back about noon and had our tents pitched, a fire going, and everything shipshape, in spite of the continuous downpour, before dark. We are taking no patients, so Johnny, George, Trogh, and I decided to get Yocky-Docky'd a bit. A lieutenant and a Captain King from one of the evacs came in looking for some nurses and joined us. This Captain King proved to be a very obnoxious individual, and we finally had to toss him out when he spit on our floor carpet (tarpaulin). All in all, it was quite an evening.

November 17, 1943—Thirty-third Field Hospital, near Presenzano

This outfit is the world's worst and is, surprisingly, getting worse all the time. I didn't think it possible. Our "rest" started today. We had visions of Naples, Capri, Sorrento, et cetera, but here we are in the rain and mud with Jerry shelling every night, us eating C rations three times a day, and no transportation to get the hell out. We are all thoroughly disgusted and short-tempered. Johnny and I are going to ask to be relieved. No outfit could be worse than this, I am sure. There is not even water here. No discipline, no nothing.

November 18, 1943—Eleventh Field Hospital, three miles south of Presenzano

Well, it looks like Colonel McCarty really did us some good! This

A.M. Major Bonham, from the Eleventh Field Hospital, came up and told us Fifth Army had transferred us to his outfit, thank God! We struck our tents, loaded the truck, and raced to get our tent up, which we did just before the downpour hit us. This Eleventh Field Hospital is a good outfit, and this was immediately apparent from the atmosphere of efficiency. We got our surgery ready by 8:00 P.M. and our quarters all set up. No patients came in tonight, however. We are backing up the Thirty-sixth Divison now but later will support the Third Division again, with whom we have made many very good friends.

November 19, 1943—Eleventh Field Hospital, near Presenzano
The meals here are swell, and the men are all very nice. We felt so pepped up that we all started airing our blankets, straightening up our stuff, and so forth. Had a rather nasty belly case to do this P.M., a lieutenant from Houston, Texas. We are getting along nicely now and feel much happier. Sullivan and Hoffman's teams wangled a transfer and joined us today. The four teams presently here makes a great setup. We are still hearing the near artillery, but last night I heard no Jerry shells. There was an air raid while I was operating, but nothing happened but a lot of ack-ack.

November 21, 1943—Eleventh Field Hospital, near Presenzano
Very little rain today. My belly case, the one I had done yesterday, died today, and I posted him. He had gas gangrene infection of the belly. This type of case is certainly discouraging. Makes four sure cases of belly gas infection and one probable that I have done. I felt a lot better, though, when "D-Day" Taylor brought back twenty-one letters for me from Caserta.

November 22, 1943—Eleventh Field Hospital, three miles south of Presenzano
I don't hanker for anything like last night's performance again, but I'm afraid it might be repeated. At about 9:00 P.M., a 170 mm. Jerry shell got a direct hit on our mess tent about fifty yards from us and blew our messing facilities to kingdom come. Why a lot of people weren't killed can only be explained by divine guidance or something similar. Even the boys cooking the 10:30 P.M. meal happened to be out getting water at the time. One of them got a chest wound, not too severe, and the other a minor leg wound. The others were untouched. The tent was a sieve from the fragments, as well as the stoves, tables, and supplies being demolished. A can of tomatoes landed in our doorway. We were in surgery about fifty yards, away and the noise of the

45

Direct hit on our mess tent, Eleventh Field Hospital, Nov. 22, 1943. Officers' mess table located directly over shell crater.

blast was terrific. Henry Hoffman was fixing preparations for a case and Major Snyder, Captain Jergeson, and Major Simioni from Fifth Army were visiting us when the shell struck. Also, Margaret Bourke-White, the famous *Life* photographer, was also visiting us. She showed up in the operating room after the explosion and was pretty scared looking, having lost a good bit of her sangfroid and superciliousness. Of course, the rest of us were plenty scared, too. I hated to get up off the floor because I knew another shell or two would follow. They sailed overhead a few hundred yards, hitting the Cub field back of us and killing a couple of men there. The visitors from Fifth Army Headquarters suddenly decided they had urgent business back in Caserta and took off in their jeep without further explanation. Johnny, George, Frank, and I had gathered outside our tent as soon as the two hit boys were evacuated (one of them cried piteously) when another shell sailed over. We had seen this Jerry dugout under the bank about twenty feet from my tent, and we all piled into it, never once dreaming of booby traps, snakes, scorpions, or other inhabitants until we were all in the dugout. Things quieted down after a while, and we decided to come out. Henry Hoffman was operating on a fellow, but there was nothing for us to do so I started me a foxhole in my tent, pulling my bedroll in, and slept okay the rest of the night, in spite of more shells whistling and exploding in the vicinity. I believe that the shell hitting us was a "short" designed for the Piper Cub field behind us.

November 23, 1943—Eleventh Field Hospital

The wreckage of the mess tent is fearful to behold, and there is a good-sized crater in the officers' mess corner. Boy, if it had landed about 10:30 P.M. instead of 9:00 P.M., there would have been a lot of dead majors and captains lying about. This afternoon, three Jerry planes came up from the south, one flying about thirty feet above the ground with his motor cut off. Don't know whether the ack-ack had hit him or whether he was just sneaking along. He drew very little fire and passed only seventy-five yards from us. Tonight, the shells are whistling in again, and I was on duty. Both times I was called over to see a patient while the shells whistled over. Fortunately, both patients were in good enough shape to send back to the evacs. This stuff scares me, and I am frank enough to admit it. The rest of the guys, Johnny, George, Trogh, and Joe, are as jittery or more jittery than I, so I guess I'm not abnormal. One shell hit within a hundred yards of us, and a piece of shrapnel came through the admission tent. Nobody hurt, fortunately. Trogh and I spent all afternoon digging us deluxe foxholes that would take our cots and beds enmasse and still leave us fifteen inches below the surface. The other boys caught the idea, and soon everyone was digging. It rains every day off and on, which makes things further disagreeable. Mud is in our beds, all over our clothes, and everywhere else. This morning, the Bourke-White gal took our miserable pictures as we were eating our breakfast of cold K rations. As an afterthought, I hope that the pictures are no good because I can imagine what M.W. will feel like if she sees them.

November 24, 1943—Eleventh Field Hospital, three miles south of Presenzano

This outfit has done a swell job of getting straightened out after the shelling, and everything is normal again. Johnny Adams and I are taking the night shift so we borrowed Henry Hoffman's jeep this afternoon and took our laundry down the road. We got hold of an ex-American Italian named Jim Kelly who claimed his "woman" was an expert laundress, so we left the laundry with him. Went on down to the Third Division Clearing Station and saw Stewart and the other boys, visiting them awhile. Met a Capt. Marcellus Johnston from Roanoke who is with the Third Division Collecting Company. Johnny Adams and I are planning to go to Naples tomorrow to see Colonel Jim Forsee about getting relieved for a couple of weeks. We have been with the artillery seventy-six days straight now and feel the need of relaxing a bit.

November 25, 1943—Eleventh Field Hospital, near Presenzano
We got up early, borrowed a jeep, and Johnny, Trogh, Frank Hoffrichter, and I set out for Naples to find Colonel Forsee, whom we had heard had arrived in Italy. We found the whole Second Aux. at the 1940 World Fairgrounds west of Naples. They are all glad to see us and had thousands of questions to ask. We certainly look like a bunch of bums, with our muddy clothes, unpressed uniforms, steel helmets, and fatigued appearance. Johnny even wore a nice, bloody pair of pants. In contrast, they were all wearing nice, clean uniforms, overseas hats, and even blouses. The colonel was exceptionally nice to us and very sympathetic, promising to relieve us for a rest. Before dinner, Gene Caldwell gave Johnny and me a couple of slugs of Scotch, which was really a treat. The colonel took us to his Thanksgiving dinner, which was swell, turkey and all the trimmings. We came back soon after dinner, arriving in a fierce wind and rain storm. There was another turkey dinner awaiting here at the Eleventh Hospital, which we ate also. Actually, I didn't realize it was Thanksgiving until we got in Naples, but I am sure thankful to be alive and well.

November 26, 1943—Eleventh Field Hospital, three miles south of Presenzano
We are still vigorously shelling Mount Camino and LaDefensa all day and night, besides dive-bombing it at intervals, which is all plainly visible to us from here. Tonight, Caserta and Naples were bombed by the Jerries and we could see the ack-ack and searchlights to the south of us. A few planes passed over us but none lingered. Bombing is nothing compared to shelling, believe me! Casualties have fortunately been light lately, so we haven't done much. This is no place for patients! We went down the road a few miles this P.M. for my laundry, but, as anticipated, it wasn't ready. This sleeping in foxholes sure makes for a sense of security.

November 27, 1943—Eleventh Field Hospital, near Presenzano
Two consultants, Major John Stewart (of Monroe, North Carolina and Buffalo, New York) and a Major Harry Beecher, who is the head of the anesthesia department of Massachusetts General Hospital, were here today, and we went over our cases with them and discussed this

48

and that. Major Stewart had never seen Long Toms so we walked a hundred yards back and watched the boys at our battery fire a few rounds. The visitors are both swell fellows and listen attentively to what we had to say from experiences we have gained. Stewart and I particularly had a long discussion regarding colostomies, anastomoses, wound closures, et cetera. Tonight, a chest case came in, bleeding actively. At my invitation, Beecher gave the anesthetic and I used Steward freely as a consultant while I did the patient. Everything went well, fortunately, and I got some nice compliments. These visitors came up in garrison hats but soon got the idea and wear their helmets as much as we do, besides sleeping in foxholes.

November 28, 1943—Eleventh Field Hospital, near Presenzano
Further discussions with Stewart and Beecher this morning. Went for my laundry again, three miles back down the road and got it. The Italians were quite excited. A shell had landed in a nearby village and they were very upset. The Army has moved the Cub airfield back five miles to where they will be safer. They decided it was too dangerous here. However, hospitals don't seem to matter. We are still bombing and shelling Mt. Camino and LaDefensa. The phosphorus shells bursting on the crest are very beautiful, really, that is, from a distance. Madding, Russell, Paul Kennedy and Weiss visited us about 2:00 P.M. so when Jerry started throwing a few air bursts on the road a couple of miles forward, they abruptly decided that they had best get back to Headquarters for early chow. Got a haircut from an adopted Wop, and looked in the mirror to see the results. Was surprised to see the amount of gray hair I have recently acquired. I wonder why?

November 29, 1943—Eleventh Field Hospital
Cloudy, rainy, and cold today and nothing much doing. Johnny and I were off from 4:00 P.M. until 8:00 A.M., so we went Yocky-Docky. Frank, George, Johnny, Trogh, and I participated in this little party. In the course of the evening, we had some involved discussions of precious gems, women's attitudes, gas gangrene, the war, and what have you.

December 1, 1943—Eleventh Field Hospital, south of Presenzano
It cleared off cold this morning, and this afternoon wave after wave of B-26s, B-25s, and A-36s went over and bombed the Jerries on the back side of Mount LaDefensa. There must have been at least 200 sorties. The planes were visible throughout the bombing runs, but were too distant to see the bombs fall. The rumble of their explosions and

clouds of brownish smoke showed us what was happening, however. Tonight at dusk, the massed artillery really opened up on Mount LaDefensa and Mount Camino and have continued to pulverize it until now. It is a fearsome sight to see the constant explosions all over the mountain. The recoil and blast from nearby guns cause the ground to shake, the tents to flap, and, in general, the din is awful.

December 2, 1943—Eleventh Field Hospital

I thought I had seen about as concentrated an artillery barrage and heavy air attacks as was possible yesterday, but today topped it by far. For a change, the skies were perfectly cloudless, and after the usual A.M. Spit patrol had come over, waves of medium bombers came from the east and unloaded. The Jerry A.A. was woefully weak, and we didn't see a single plane knocked down. This bombing continued all day with a lull at noon. There were well over 200 bombers and these in flights of 12. The A-36 type bombed Jerry all day, must have been between 400 and 500 sorties. Don't see how anyone could stand it. Tonight at 6:10 P.M., the artillery really let go. There are reported to be seven hundred fieldpieces trained on Mount LaDefensa and Mount Camino. They all fired as fast and furiously as they could. This mountain was literally alive with shell bursts. I believe practically every inch of the mountains was hit. Nothing could live in it, I am sure, except Germans and they in their dugouts. The British on our left even had tracer Bofors antiaircraft firing steady streams at the mountains. Well, this was the first time I had heard firing that was a continuous roar, and the flashing of the guns made it quite light outside. In fact, I could have read a newspaper had I had one. Our four close batteries of Long Toms sounded like the Anvil Chorus, they were shooting so fast. We hear that the Rangers from the Aleutians are taking part in the attack on these mountains tonight and, we also hear, the Special Service Forces, made up mostly of United States and Canadian misfits, but good fighting men, the main offensive unit. These mountains have held us up in this one spot for twenty-eight days straight to my personal knowledge. This mountain massif to the west of us extends from the Volturno to the Garigliano and Liri valleys, a distance of twelve to fifteen miles. The side facing us (the east face) is precipitous and sheer, but the west side (the German side) is gently sloping and can be supplied easily by motor transportation. Also, motorized artillery can run up at night and shell this whole valley, moving from place to place so that their positions can't be pinpointed. Also, the Germans can dig in on this reverse slope. The various peaks of this massif are from south to north are called: (1) Monastery Hill, (2) Mount Camino, (3) Mount LaDefensa, (4) Mount LaRemetanea and (5) Mount Maggiore. It is

50

absolutely essential to clear these mountains before we can attack the Cassino and Gustav line.

December 3, 1943—Eleventh Field Hospital, south of Presenzano
The attack on Mount LaDefensa was successful last night, and some casualties have come in. Jerry still occupies some of the hill, however. George and I went into Caserta and ate lunch at the palace (Field Officers' Mess) with Maj. Howard Snyder, and did a few errands like trading tents, getting watches fixed, and so forth. We heard that headquarters is moved up to Marcianise, a village about three miles southwest of Caserta. We went down there and found Lt. Col. Bill Sheridan, our executive officer, Herb Moore, Cade Smith, Bill Nelson, Jack Knotts, and others getting the school ready for the group to move in. The school is a private kindergarten, with suitable tiny commodes, the proper height for kindergarten pupils. It is in the middle of a dirty little village of Marcianise. However, it isn't so bad inside. There are about five fairly nice buildings, which are clean and modern, built around a courtyard. We talked to Bill Sheridan about our needed rest, needed transportation, et cetera. He was very nice about it all. By the time we started back, it was raining and foggy, not a pleasant trip. Arrived back about dark. The artillery is still firing spasmodically, but over the mountain.

December 4, 1943—Eleventh Field Hospital
Was I chagrined today! I got up for breakfast at 7:00 A.M., did what work there was to be done in the postoperative wards, and finished about 10:00 A.M. It was pouring rain and I got sleepy, so I crawled down into my foxhole for a snooze. About 11:30 A.M., I heard someone yelling outside, "Can I come in?"; and who should it be but Colonel Forsee and Mansfield! I sure felt foolish being in bed at that hour. Well, the colonel had dinner with us and we had a nice talk. He is relieving us very soon, but we made him promise to try to send us back to the Eleventh Field Hospital instead of the Thirty-third, when we are returned. The colonel was very jovial and friendly. Our pet guns didn't put on much of an act for him, unfortunately. The cases started rolling in about 2:00 P.M., and we worked until 10:30 P.M. Most of the poor kids have been up on the mountain for twenty-four hours, and they were sure cold and wet, besides being shot all to hell. I really don't see how any of them lived through it.

December 5, 1943—Eleventh Field Hospital
The Eagles were sure flying around today. We had an inspection and ward rounds by Colonel Churchill, the surgeon for the Fifth Army,

51

Colonel Cutler, who is consultant surgeon of the E.T.O., a Colonel Ginn, surgeon of II Corps. Colonel Churchill and Colonel Cutler complimented us on the work we are doing. Colonel Churchill impressed me as a fine and knowledgeable man, and I liked him immediately. Colonel Cutler, surgical consultant of E.T.O. and professor of surgery at Harvard, had recently visited the Russian front. He seemed more interested in discussing the beautiful yellow larches of the Russian forests than he did in surgical matters. I was disappointed in his attitude, but carefully refrained from calling it to his attention. I rather suspect that he is somewhat jealous of Colonel Churchill's observations, innovations, and influence on military matters, inasmuch as he hadn't had his first battle casualty.

Colonel Churchill had this to say about his visit in his postwar book Surgeon to Soldiers: *"The 11th Field Hospital was receiving the seriously wounded from the 36th Division and was sited near a Long-Tom battery that was firing intermittently. A shell from counter-battery fire had hit the mess tent shortly before I arrived. The surgical operations in progress were demonstrations which I was proud to have Cutler witness."*

December 6, 1943—Eleventh Field Hospital
Our pets, the four batteries of 155s, were moved up today, thank God! I feel a lot safer. It surely is strangely quiet about. There is still a bunch of 240 mm. Howitzers about one half-mile away, but they don't shoot too often. Got out of my foxhole and aboveground!

December 7, 1943—Eleventh Field Hospital
Johnny, Frank, and I borrowed Frank Hall's jeep and went to Caserta this P.M. after the mail and some medical supplies we needed so urgently, but were told that no supplies were available. I got a lot of rubber tubing and glass tubing in spite of the fact that we were told there was none to be had. I just asked for it and got it. Now we can rig up Wangensteens, intravenous sets, et cetera. That will work! The army supply outfit makes me throw up my hands in despair. No one can tell me much about the alleged efficiency of the army! We got some mail, including two letters from my wife.

December 8, 1943—Eleventh Field Hospital
Another push is reported to be under way soon. We are getting a right many casualties back, most wounded for three to four days. It is a hell of a job getting these casualties down off the mountains. We had some long hours of work.

December 9, 1943—Eleventh Field Hospital
Another severe siege of work, and I am too tired to think straight. Worked from 2:00 A.M. straight through until midnight. We had two deaths on the table within minutes of each other; our mortality rate is appalling, since we do only the most desperate cases. The death I had was due to a hole in the heart. I sure wish our relief would show up soon.

December 11, 1943—Eleventh Field Hospital
Colonel Forsee and Code Smith came by and found us busy with a bunch of sick postoperative patients. I went over the cases with Colonel Forsee. The relief will arrive in four or five days, he says.

December 12, 1943—Eleventh Field Hospital
Today, Johnny and I were on call, midnight to 8:00 A.M. shift, and had nothing much to do. We decided to celebrate Frank Hoffrichter's promotion to captain tonight, which we did. We started in about 6:00 P.M. on the Yocky-Docky. Johnny had asked Ruth Hindman and her date, a Major Strickland, over to his tent, where the party was being held. We had a hilarious time getting Ruth in a hole for an idle remark she had made that "If Joe Barrett wasn't married, I could go for him." We got Joe in the tent and debated the thing back and forth for a couple of hours. We had promised to make Frank pass out, and about 9:30 P.M., we put him to bed, literally. We assisted Johnny to bed soon after, and as I wasn't feeling too stable, I went to bed myself, with no help.

December 13, 1943—Eleventh Field Hospital
This morning I was awakened by someone hollering, "The Arabs are here! The Arabs are here!" Being somewhat fuzzy from last night's imbroglio, I staggered out of the sack and looked out the door of my tent. Johnny Adams, still somewhat stoned, was standing at his tent entrance pointing to the ground and shouting, "The Arabs are here!" Well, on investigation, it was concluded that Frank Hoffrichter had the urge to evacuate his bowels during the night and made it to the tent entrance, but no farther. Hence Johnny's outcry. Frank Hall's relief in the form of Ken Lowery's team came in today, so Frank and co-workers lost no time in getting the hell out. Most of us weren't feeling too good on account of last night. Johnny felt better when Ken said that one team was coming up Wednesday to relieve Johnny. There is no word of our relief! I began to wonder, *What the hell?*

December 14, 1943, Tuesday—Eleventh Field Hospital

This afternoon Johnny, George, Frank, and I went down the road to the 244th Italian Field Hospital, which is about a half-mile back of us. A captain was the CO, and one of our GIs acted as interpreter. They have very nice tents and excellent equipment, but as far as I could tell, most of their treatment consists of watchful waiting. Frank had our pictures taken with the Ginso docs, and they gave us a shot of very excellent cognac. They were very polite and eager to show us about. There was much heel clicking, saluting, and Dago talk. Tonight I did my first transdiaphragmatic splenectomy. Then sewed up my first dehiscence. This patient of mine, Charlie Bilbrey, is an amazing man. Charlie is a master sergeant with the 142nd Infantry of the Thirty-sixth Division. He was brought in December 8, 1943, with an extensive shell fragment wound with involvement of the buttocks, rectum with multiple compound fractures of the pelvis, besides having compound fractures of both bones of the left forearm and of the right ankle. Charlie had developed all kind of complications, including a severe anaerobic cellulitis to the right buttock and thigh. A colostomy that I had done was working satisfactorily. However, he dehisced his abdominal incision, which is mentioned above, on December 14, 1943, and I had to close it. Charlie has remained cheerful and never complains. He has developed a fine, cordial relationship with me.

Wednesday, December 15, 1943—Eleventh Field Hospital

Well, Fishwick and his team pulled in about noon, and it didn't take long for Johnny and his team to get out. It's a good thing they did! I went to bed about 11:00 P.M., and about that time, two shells came in a mile or so away, so I lowered my bed to the floor. About that time, a shell landed near enough to hear the shrapnel whine, so I didn't lose any time in throwing my cot in the foxhole, piling my bedroll on top of it, and getting underground myself. I was sure glad I did, because it wasn't but a few minutes until the crashing shriek of a shell that landed within a hundred yards of us, and that is too close. This shelling sure scares the hell out of me. Bombing and strafing are nothing compared to shelling. You keep lying there, listening for the distant boom of a Jerry gun, then holding your breath for about three seconds until the "cr-r-ump" of the exploding shell tells you that another had missed you. If they hit close, they have a sort of crashing shriek when they go off, the sound being prolonged by the supersonic flight of the fragments. About five nights ago, Jerry shelled us, and one did sound like it scraped our stovepipe, it hit so close. The ground shook even though it was a dud and didn't go off. A lot more whistled overhead, and if you don't think it is a bloodcurdling sound, just ask someone who's heard it. I got called out at 3:00 A.M. tonight to do a belly case. These cases give you enough worry without wondering where the next shell's going to hit. Fortunately, none hit very close, but they kept coming in until 4:00 A.M. I love a foxhole in spite of the dirt, cold, and wetness. It seems that Jerry runs up track-mounted artillery pieces behind the ridge of mountains at the northern end of Mount Camino, fires five or six rounds from one position, scoots to another position, and fires some more, so that our artillery never can catch up with them. It is harrassing fire and thrown around indiscriminately, which is the worst kind as far as I'm concerned. I am ready to be relieved!

December 16, 1943—Eleventh Field Hospital
This afternoon, an extraordinary parade took place on the road (Highway 6) that runs 100 yards from our hospital. Truckload after truckload of Italian troops went by, all the troops whooping, hollering, waving Italian flags, and singing at the top of their lungs. One would think that they were bound for a glorious holiday rather than going to the front lines. The contrast with these troops and American troops is startling: instead of indulging in the type of antics exhibited by the Italians, American troops being transported to the front all sit quietly, grim-faced and serious.

We hear that the Italians are going to take Mount Lungo, which is a small mountain and the stopper in the Mignano Gap between Mount Maggiore to the west and Mount Rotundo to the east.

The Italians made their attack on Mount Lungo a day or two after I was sent back to Headquarters, and they got the hell kicked out of them. This was the last time the Italians were used as combat troops as far as I know. On revisiting this area in 1975, I found that the Italians had constructed an elaborate memorial cemetery at the beginning of the ascent to Horseshoe Bend on Mount Lungo in commemoration of this inglorious action. This whole Mignano Gap area and its approaches has been dubbed "Purple Heart Valley" by the correspondents of the media. It does seem rather appropriate!

December 17, 1943—Eleventh Field Hospital
I got my stuff ready and took care of most things by the time Brinker and his team arrived to relieve us. We were pretty happy and somewhat relieved to see Herb and his team. We managed to extricate our tarp in spite of violent protestations on Herb's part. We turned our patients over to Herb. Charlie Bilbrey sure hated to see me go, and his farewell was very touching. This is one guy I hope gets well! We

Mount Maggiori Masif defending Mignano Gap. Also shown: Mount Lungo, Mount Porchia, Mount Trocchio, and Liri Valley.

left about 2:00 P.M. and arrived at Headquarters about 4:00 P.M. Everyone seemed glad to see us, but we felt sort of our of place with our field clothing, very dirty. There is no heat in our rooms, and it is pretty miserable. After supper, Gene Caldwell, Johnny, and I got out the Yocky-Docky and kept going until 2:00 A.M., hovering over my Primus stove for warmth, discussing everything under the sun.

December 18, 1943—Headquarters, Marcianise
Joe and I went into Naples this morning and looked around through the shops. Went to Bari's and got some gloves. We got hooked up with an English-speaking Italian somehow, who took us here and there. Naples has changed a great deal since we left here. All shops and stores are open now, and every one is a jewelry store. They have all the same line of junk. There are billions of cameos, all at exorbitant prices. We went to a little native restaurant just off the Via Roma for lunch that this Italian "guide" recommended. The food was really excellent, very flavorsome after the GI diet, and we got some wine called Orvieto, which was really delicious. We drank three bottles of it and were feeling

pretty good after lunch. We had a lot of fun going through these stores and telling these non–English speaking Italians just what we thought of them, their practices, their prices, and everything else. No doubt the Orvieto had something to do with this maneuver. We finally wound up taking nice showers and getting shaves, haircuts, and shoeshines. Feeling like new men, we went back to headquarters and froze some more.

December 19, 1943—Marcianise

A quite dull day. This afternoon a bunch of us went up to the King's palace for a shower, which the engineers have erected about two miles from the palace at the distal end of the royal gardens. The gardens are really magnificent running back to this area. They rival the Versailles Gardens, it is said. Apparently, the Italians pipe water from the mountains down to this high hill, where it emerges and moves down a couple of hundred feet to a large pool filled with statues et cetera. From there to the palace two miles away, there are formal gardens, pools, fountains, masonry of artistic sorts, statuary, and what have you. We also went through the part of the palace that has been cleaned up and saw a lot of interesting paintings, with much raucous comments about the depicted nudity from the accompanying brethren.

December 20, 1943—Headquarters at Marcianise

I can't get warm here in spite of long johns and layers of clothing. Got a lot of Christmas packages, although fed up with candy now. I haven't tasted anything that is quite so good as the green tomato chow-chow, cheese, and crackers Mary Will sent me. She certainly knows what I like. These gustatorial knickknacks are quite a relief from the usual army fare of dehydrated eggs, dehydrated potatoes, dehydrated onions, entirely tasteless Spam, Vienna sausage, canned beans, powdered milk, and similar great inventions. Mess call is something one feels one should be attended, but more as a duty rather than a pleasure. Thank God they have decent coffee! Anyhow, the whole outfit is chuckling over an episode that took place a day or two ago between "Smiley" Blocksom (Maj. Beret H. Blocksom, Jr, from Louisiana) and Colonel Forsee. Smiley is a lean, gangly guy with a continuous dour and sour mien, who never smiles but expresses his disfavor of the world in general and the army in particular in a straightforward and profane manner, hence the inevitable nickname Smiley. Anyhow, he was called before Colonel Forsee a day or so ago and asked the question, "Major Blocksom, it has been reported to me that you called our food slop. Is that true?" "No, sir," said Smiley. "It's a damn lie. I did not call it slop. I called it swill." The food did get a little better thereafter. *Nicknames were widely applied to a lot of our officers, and many were called only by their nicknames. For example, Smiley Blocksom, who never smiled, Sorehead Poole, who was always affable and always smiling, Curley Sittler, who was a real cue-ball, and so on. Even Colonel Forsee was called Colonel Foreskin by some of his command, but not to his face. I was universally referred to and called Geechie which cognomen was started by Trogh Adkins. He said that I was undoubtedly descended from the Ogeechee Indians of Eastern Georgia, these Indians being rather looked down upon.*

December 21, 1943—Headquarters, Marcianise
Having remembered seeing a lot of evergreens around Maddaloni, I mentioned the fact when I heard one of our nurses, Miss Henshaw, moaning about her three-foot Christmas tree. I was stuck then, so we got a weapons carrier, rode until we saw some guy's ornamental hedge of cedars, and went in. With lots of gestures and finally with falling back on my high school French, I think, I said, "Je vieux un arbre." Somehow this finally got through to him. He was very agreeable, being an "Officiale Italiani" of Naples. So we whacked down the most symmetrical tree, giving the others a chance to grow. He showed us where he and four others were hidden seventy-five feet down in a cistern when the Germans were around. The nurses were delighted with this big tree and decorated it with whatever they could contrive after it was put up.

December 22, 1943—Marcianise
I heard that Curley Sittler was going to Naples so I went along, primarily to get some wine in which to soak my fruitcake, which Mary Will had sent me. We went to the little restaurant, and I was able to get three bottles of Orvieto. We also had dinner there. After dinner, we set out for Sorrento to pick up Johnny, George, and Frank, who had been stranded there for twenty-four hours. Walsh was in front, and Curley was acting as navigator. After about one and one-half hours, we suddenly discovered we were back in Salerno, so there was nothing to do but backtrack forty miles and head out on the Amalfi drive for Sorrento. The Sorrentine Peninsula is beautiful and picturesque. It is very mountainous, the road being cut out of stone, and everywhere possible there is a villa or some such building perched. We wound up at the Hotel Vittorio in Salerno about dark, so we stayed, had a couple of "Vesuvio" cocktails, and ate dinner there. There was an orchestra, folk dancing, singing, and the whole works, including ice cream and cake. The ride back was rough, but all in all it was a satisfactory day.

December 23, 1943

More Christmas packages came in, and I have enough things almost to start a delicatessen. Needless to say, we all enjoy these goodies very much indeed. I guess the folks back home think something of us, all right. We had a meeting of all the team captains to iron out difficulties. This afternoon we went up to a head injury meeting in Caserta. Nothing of consequence came of it. Charlie Dowman made somewhat of an ass of himself. Saw Colonel Sanzane, Major Rife, Major Patterson, and others, who were all very friendly. Colonel Sanzane wanted me to come up to the Ninety-fourth Evac, but I was forced to say, "No, thanks. I prefer a field hospital."

December 24, 1943—Marcianise

There was a skit tonight and a show put on by the various talented members of the command. We enjoyed the good cracks in it. The one they wanted to put on riding Colonel Forsee was a lulu, but it was vetoed by the executive officer, Bill Sheriden. After the show, I went to Caserta to the 10:00 P.M. church and communion. It was quite nice, being held in what was apparently a movie hall. The altar was set up just in front of a hole made by a shell hit. The roof, which had been blown off, was again covered. A rather strange setting, to be sure. Got home about midnight and went to bed in spite of many celebrations going on.

December 25, 1943—Headquarters, Marcianise

We started having our Christmas party at about 10:00 A.M., and from boredom and loneliness for the family, I joined in rather heartily. By the time Christmas dinner was ready, we were caroling in full voice. We had a swell dinner; so they tell me. After dinner, I found myself very tired and slept until supper. We had a dance tonight, with *beaucoup* cognac and wine. The high spot of the evening was Joe Barrett's jitterbugging. After the party, Curley Sittler, Ernie Rose, and I sat around until 3:30 A.M., imbibing and singing robust songs, much to the annoyance of guys who hadn't passed out.

December 27, 1943—Albergo Vittoria, Sorrento

Joe and I came down in a command car, arriving just before lunch. We had a nice tub bath, cleaned up, and took a nap before lunch. Possible the couple of double "Vesuvios" had something to do with the nap. Just as we were going down to supper, ran into Lacore coming up the stairs and were invited up to Room 24 by this Lieutenant Colonel he was with. There we had a few rounds of "Sarti" and water, which isn't like Scotch and soda, but the best we could do. We all had supper together and then sat talking at our table. Other people had the same idea, and it soon turned into a spontaneous dance, interspersed with acts from the orchestra, the singer, and dancers. Incidentally, this little singer has a voice that is remarkable for a soprano, with volume, ease, clarity, and tone. Besides being as cute as she can be. Reminds me of my little daughter, Mary Louise, in her actions for some reason. After the dance broke up at midnight, we adjourned to Mac's room, Room 24, and had a bull session. Mac is Lt. Col. Frank McCulloch, Battalion Commander, Thirty-fourth Division, from Excelsior, Minnesota. We found that we agreed on most points. We talked war mostly, and Mac, who has had two battlefield promotions, told of his sensations and bitter feelings at seeing his men killed and wounded and of his sensations while under fire for weeks on end. Joe and I knew how he felt, although to a much lesser degree. We even helped him elaborate. Some of the other men present who had not been under fire obviously didn't and couldn't understand these reactions, and it is a mistake to discuss these matters before such individuals. They just don't understand or grasp it, and from their eyes, it is easy to tell they think you are just putting it on, even though it's your most sincere feelings. The meeting broke up about 4:00 A.M., at least that's when I broke it off.

December 28, 1943—Albergo Vittoria, Sorrento
Joe and I had to move out of our room, No. 21, and found a room out in town in the archbishop's house. He is very poor, but his place is clean and has modern plumbing. He tries to please us so much it is pathetic to hear him keep crying that he loves the Americans. We ran into Major Boylan, CO of the First Platoon of the Eleventh Field Hospital, and had a few drinks with him and Mac and adjourned to McCulloch's room. We decided to form the "24 Club" (Mac's room number) for the purpose of intellectual discussions and moderate imbibing. Mac asked General Caffey up, and we made him a member. General Caffey is commanding general of the Thirty-fourth Division and is bitterly disappointed at being relieved from his command because of apparently a mild Buerger's disease.

December 29, 1943—Sorrento
Got up early this morning although it was quite a chore. Mac and I went on the trip to Capri. Joe Barrett just couldn't make it. The boat trip over is very nice, giving a splendid view of the Bay of Naples, Vesuvius, Ischia, and the Sorrentine Peninsula and Capri. We piled in a "Fiat" at the landing place and toured the island. To Anacapri, over a winding, precipitous road, and to the south side of the island, where

we got a boat and took a trip to the Grotto Verde, an old Roman grotto and bathing place and to those huge rocks, the Faragliones. We ate lunch and had a couple of drinks at the Quinsetta (?), an air corps hotel. We returned to the Albergo Vittoria and had a meeting of the 24 Club. This meeting broke up about 2:00 A.M. Joe went to sleep and snored at the meeting.

December 30, 1943, Sorrento

Succeeded in getting Joe up this A.M., and Mac, Joe, and I visited Pompeii. The ruins were much more extensive and complete than I had anticipated. I enjoyed the trip. There seems to be something a bit fishy in the perfect preservations of the pornograpic art in the whorehouse and in the Brothers Vetti House, but there was some very nice art in the carvings otherwise; the baths, waterworks and lead pipe, sewage disposal, et cetera were amazing. They seem far better than the average Italian stuff of today. We ate a very poor lunch in Pompeii and then visited the cathedral, which is very ornate and costly with donated panels of silver pictures all over the place. Returned to the Albergo Vittoria in late afternoon, had a nap and a meeting of the 24 Club and dinner.

December 31, 1943—Sorrento, Italy

We were supposed to go back to headquarters today, but no one showed up to pick us up. Mac McCulloch went back, and did he hate to go! I don't blame him. He has seen enough and done enough for one man, but I suppose it has to be. We stayed over for the party and dance tonight.

January 1, 1944—Headquarters, Marcianise

We sat around the hotel lobby at Sorrento all morning, ate New Year's dinner, and still no one showed up for us. We bummed a ride back in a jeep with a lieutenant going up to Presenzano. It was a mean ride, terrific, cold wind, sleet, and rain. When we got back we found that both the Eleventh Field Hospital and the Thirty-third Field Hospital had blown down in a howling windstorm. The teams were being returned to headquarters, hence our lack of transportation.

January 4, 1944—Eleventh Field Hospital, First Platoon, two miles southwest of Presenzano

This morning, I slept late, thinking I would get up about 9:30 A.M., cook the egg (the only fresh egg I have had since leaving headquarters back in Bizerta, Africa, August 25, 1943). This particular egg was given to me by a washwoman to whom I had given some candy. Was my mouth watering! Just as I started to get up, the orderly came in and said the colonel wanted to see me, so I got up and went to see him. He said I was to go up to the First Platoon of the Eleventh Field Hospital, Major Boylan's outfit. Bill Edwards's team was to go up in lieu of Johnny Adams, since Johnny had this infected finger for over two months that would not heal. Gordon Madding and Henry Hoffman's teams are already up there. I am to be chief of surgical service, since I am ranking officer. I talked the situation over with Joe Barrett, who has been having a hard time, and went to see the colonel. We all decided Joe ought to have a physical checkup, so I had to leave him behind, much as I hated to do so. I got, as his replacement, Charlie Westerfield. Charlie is a really good anesthesiologist from Savannah, Georgia, besides being a swell fellow. Actually it will be easier on me because I won't have to watch the patient so closely. Arnold decided he wanted to try to get in the air corps, so I was given Sergeant Dunlap in his place. Dunlap is a good surgical technician. We rushed to get ready and pulled out about 11:30 A.M. The nearer we got to the front, the muddier it got. We found the Eleventh Field Hospital about a quarter-mile down the road and across from the place where we had left the Thirty-third Field Hospital six weeks ago. It shows what progress has been made in this war!

We are backing up the Thirty-sixth Division now. They said there had been no shelling back in this area since December 15, 1943, so we merrily pitched our tent in the mud and got set up. I turned in about 11:00 P.M. and woke up with a start about 1:00 A.M. thinking I had dreamed I heard a shell exploding and shrapnel whine. I was reassured by Trogh and Westerfield, who had come in from the visit of the Ninety-fourth Evac, that I really wasn't dreaming. About that time, the old whistling cr-r-ump of exploding shells nearby went again. So we all plopped on the floor and wished fervently for our foxholes. There was nothing to do but sweat it out. There was more shelling about 4:30 A.M. and again about 6:00 A.M. Most of them overhead exploding back of us. I slept very poorly, and our artillery rumbled all night. A push is on to take Mount Maggiore and Mount Lungo, but this harassing fire keeps on and on.

January 5, 1944—Eleventh Field Hospital, two miles south of Presenzano

And on top of everything else, the damndest windstorm has been blowing all day without cessation. We double anchored our tent, but it still is dubious as to whether it will stay up. One just can't keep these tents warm in spite of red-hot stoves. The casualties are still pouring in, and all the teams are working their entire shift of sixteen hours, being off eight hours. My working period ended at 4:00 A.M., and I was quite tired. These poor kids are frozen when they are brought in, and it is criminal to operate on them in that cold operating tent, but it can't be helped.

January 6, 1944—Eleventh Field Hospital
The wind is dying down today, but it sure is cold. Puddles of water didn't even thaw. Casualties still very severe and more than we can handle. These boys are mostly from the Sixth Armored Regiment, who had been used as regular infantry, trying to take Mount Porchio. It is reported that the tanks are taking off today, but in such weather and mud, I don't see how they can do much. Worked until 1:30 A.M. on my shift and then got to help Gordon Madding take out a tough spleen. Got to bed about 4:00 A.M.

Gordon Madding is one of my Mayo Clinic friends. He was a second assistant when I was Jim Priestey's first assistant. He is an excellent surgeon and likes to work, thank heavens.

January 7, 1944—Eleventh Field Hospital
Casualties still pouring in. I worked from four until four, having the worst case I believe I have had yet: a British lad with his left thigh blown off level with his body and extensive other wounds. Boy, was he a mess. He was hit by a 40 mm. antiaircraft shell accidentally. Colonel Forsee came around today asking everyone if they wanted to go on the next tea party (invasion). I said, bluntly, "No." I wanted no part of it, but told him whatever he wanted me to do was okay. Everyone said about the same thing, essentially. Considerable German shelling about two miles up the valley tonight while we were working, but none hit very close.

January 8, 1944—Eleventh Field Hospital, near Presenzano
We worked all last night, finishing at 5:40 A.M. Trogh, Charlie, and I came over to our tent and made Nescafe, toast, and jam for an early breakfast. Then to bed until noon.

January 11, 1944—Eleventh Field Hospital
We have had practically no cases for the past two or three days, and I am beginning to think that the Sixth Armored Infantry is either all wiped out or else captured. *P.S.: They took Mount Porchio.*

January 12, 1944—Eleventh Field Hospital

Finally got some swell letters from Mary Will, and did I need them! Still very quiet, with no patients coming in. Our artillery has moved up until they are barely audible. Every night we have a feed about midnight. We do very well with toast, cheese, butter, coffee, and jam. I am afraid I will get fat again oh, me! The Thirty-sixth Division is replacing the Sixth Armored Regiment, and Cassino has not yet fallen. Over the past two and a half months, we have seen the Third Division, the Sixth Armored, and the Thirty-sixth Division shot up more than somewhat, going about ten miles distance, within this period.

January 14, 1944

Trogh woke me up sometime in the early morning hours to listen to German guns go boom, followed by the crunch of shells exploding a couple of miles up the valley. I wish they would do something about our left flank, where the British were drinking tea and dragging their heels. Bill Sheriden, Smitty, and Curley came up today, and I had to sign for all the tents, trucks, stoves, et cetera, being the senior officer. I will never be able to pay for all this stuff.

January 15, 1944—Eleventh Field Hospital

Word came this morning that we were to move up one and one-half miles to the Third Platoon of the Eleventh Field Hospital (Major Bonham's), so as busy as little beavers, we got all packed up by noon and started to strike our tents. Then, as usual, came the word to hold everything. So I got in the truck and drove up to the area we were supposed to go, just opposite the road to Presenzano where it turns off Highway 6. The Third Platoon had pitched their tents, but no one was around. Apparently, the advance toward Cassino has been rapid enough to warrant our moving up farther. I am getting to be a fair six-by-six truck driver, double clutching and down shifting without too much clashing of gears. We unpacked our bedrolls, got our tents up and stoves set up again, and waited. Worked all night tonight.

January 17, 1944—Eleventh Field Hospital

Maj. Gen. Ernest Cowell, surgeon of all medical forces in Italy, visited us, and I went over the patients with him. He seemed very pleased with the work we were doing and, surprisingly enough, knew a lot about surgery and took an active interest in the professional side of it, which is very unusual in a high-ranking officer. He is English and very friendly. He kept telling me about what he used to do in WWI when he was a surgeon in a forward area. He is recommending the whole Second Aux. Unit for a commendation. Worked again tonight.

January 18, 1944—Eleventh Field Hospital

Two miles south of Presenzano, we are still living out of Musette bags, waiting to move. The infantry of the Thirty-sixth Division is now on the left bank of the Rapido River, and we are getting an epidemic of horrible mine wounds with traumatic amputations of one or both legs. The Germans are using a new type of nonmetallic mine called "shue mines," which cannot be detected except by probing. "Teller" and "Bouncing Betsy" mines are bad enough, but these little shue mines are worse. One lad with a leg off told me he stepped on the first mine while putting a rubber raft in the river for a patrol. Litter bearers came up; one of them stepped on another mine, and another leg was lost. A doctor came up, stepped on still another mine, and was killed. This seems a very inhumane type of warfare and certainly causes trying and difficult wounds. We have had five patients in with traumatic amputations during the last twenty-four hours. Major Howard Snyder and Colonel Holtz, who is the Norwegian surgeon general, have been visiting us for the past two days, observing. We had quite a little show for them, and the colonel thanked me after a couple of cases I did, just like being back in civilian surgery. Colonel Holtz said later (see preface in the surgeon general's publication *Surgery in W.W. II,* Volume 2): "You are holding to the standard of university clinic surgery under fire and in tents with mud floors."

January 19, 1944—Eleventh Field Hospital, Horsehoe Bend of Mount Lungo

We were not doing much today, so at 3:00 P.M. Charlie Westerfield and I got in a truck to start down the road for a shower, when they yelled at us to report at once to the Third Platoon of the Eleventh Field Hospital. Gordon and his team drew lots to be the holding unit. The rest of us hurriedly packed up, tore down our tents, and madly loaded. We went up Highway 6 for about eight miles, past Mignano, or what remains of it, and passed a German defense position in front of Mount Lungo where three of our tanks really got knocked about. The Jerries have dug trenches and cut all trees, et cetera, for field of fire. Arrived at our new location just at dusk. It was useless to try to get set up, so we slept in the ward tent. Fortunately, no patients came in. I don't know why we seem to always have to arrive at a new location about dark! We have a nice location, however. A high meadow in a pass one mile south of San Pietro-in-Fine. Mount Sammucro towers over us to the north. Fairly high hills are all around us, which will afford us some defilade, I hope.

January 20, 1944—Eleventh Field Hospital, Mt. Lungo

I got up early, and Scotty and I went back to Headquarters to exchange two bad tents and take care of other business. It was nice to see Joe Barrett, Johnny Adams, and George Donaghy again. The boys for the web-foot invasion have either gone or have been restricted. Got back up here just at dark, after stopping at Major Boylan's platoon for some fine fried chicken. Trogh and Charlie had set up our tent. Had a patient come in after we got back and shortly before midnight, and by the time we got him in shape and worked on, the night was gone. We still didn't get to go to bed, for there was another case to do. Finally went to bed about 11:00 P.M.

January 21, 1944—Mount Lungo

Were rudely awakened at 4:00 A.M. by the old, familiar scream of overhead shells. They were shelling the road back of us, with occasional shells up near San Pietro and even some shells on the hills around us, but our defilade seemed to work, as the worst we got was some falling stone in the area from a shell burst on one of the hills near us. The noise of these shells hitting on the surrounding hills really does cause a terrific crash. The German guns firing sound extremely close. We got down on the floor near our stove, having no foxholes, and sweated it out until we pretty nearly froze. After about half an hour of shelling, I started counting shells exploding and going overhead. I counted 106 shells, of which 31 were "duds" and the rest exploded. Don't know why the Germans have so many duds, but I am thankful they do. Slave labor imperfections? After the shelling stopped, I drifted off to sleep for an hour or so, but was called early to see cases. Colonel Ginn, the new II Corps surgeon, came in. We had six patients in shock and two in surgery, so he got a bit excited and called Colonel Forsee for help. Jim Sullivan and his team arrived this afternoon. The boys in the Thirty-sixth Division are trying to cross the Rapido River and are taking a real shellacking. Casualties severe and heavy. Major Snyder and Colonel Holtz came up and have been observing.

January 22, 1944—Mount Lungo

This was a rough day. Henry Hoffman called on me to do a case involving the perineum and abdomen at 8:00 A.M., which was really an exhausting procedure. There were six more cases to be done. We finished up about 1:00 A.M. Mike Mason, Lt. Col., who is professor of surgery at Northwestern University, and Colonel Forsee showed up about 4:00 P.M., and we really showed them what work was like up here. I think they were duly impressed. They hung on to the bitter end, and I even had Mike Mason hold a leg for me while I amputated it. The visitors slept here, and as usual, when Colonel Forsee is around, it was an extremely quiet night. I am surely getting tired again.

January 23, 1944—Horseshoe Bend on Mount Lungo
The news of the landing up at Anzio has come through and it sounds okay, but this occurrence didn't deter Jerry. He made a counterattack across the Rapido River. We are four and half miles from the nearest point, and there is more Jerry shelling north and south of us than I have ever heard. What really alarmed us was the sound of German machine pistols and the "screaming meemies." The latter go who-o-, who-o-o, who-o-o, with a hissing note on each who-o-o. It is the first time we have heard small arms fire since the beachhead. A case came in just after I got to bed. I got up and finally did him, finishing about 6:00 A.M. This patient was a lieutenant from Lincoln, North Carolina, with belly wounds and compound fractures of both femora.

January 25, 1944—Horseshoe Bend on Mount Lungo
Got a bunch of the swellest letters from Mary Will. There is no better tonic for my well-being. It was quiet today, thank heavens, and we got caught up on our sleep somewhat, athough the postoperative patient care keeps us plenty busy.

January 26, 1944—Horseshoe Bend on Mount Lundo
Henry Hoffman went back to headquarters today and came back with the dreadful news that the hospital ship on which Johnny Adams was assigned had been sunk and that Johnny and McCombs (one of his enlisted men, and a swell kid) were unaccounted for. I was very shocked and depressed at this news, since I considered Johnny one of my best friends, and I only hope and pray that they were rescued but are not reported yet. Jergy came up and I had him see a patient (a Lieutenant Vigneau) who was suspicious of gas infection of his amputation stump. We decided it was an Oedematians infections, so I had to reamputate him through the thigh. Otherwise not much work today.

January 27, 1944—Eleventh Field Hospital, Horseshoe Bend on Mount Lungo
The news about Johnny is true, and from the accounts of two of our nurses, Ruth Hindman and Bess Berret, who were rescued, it looks as if Johnny had no chance whatsoever. The hospital ships had pulled out from Anzio about twelve miles at dusk and turned on their lights.

About half an hour later, Jerry bombers came over and dropped flares and dive-bombed all three ships. The *St. David*, the ship Johnny was on, was hit right away. The nurses said they just felt and heard a thud and were not particularly alarmed. Johnny even helped Ruth get her lifebelt on and told her to go up on deck. She asked him if he wasn't coming, too. He said, "No, I am going down to see about the patients." Ruth went on deck at once, and the crew yelled for her to jump. Only one lifeboat had been lowered; she jumped just in time, and as she came up, the ship sank in less than five minutes after it had been hit. Apparently it capsized before sinking. If Johnny did go below, there is certainly no hope for him. McCombs was never seen at all, being seasick in his quarters well down in the ship. The whole bottom of the ship must have been blown out. The other two ships were bombed repeatedly, and the *Leinstern* was hit but not badly. The *Leinstern* and the *St. Andrews* picked up the survivors from the *St. David*, including our nurses. The nurses were in the water about an hour, and aside from being very cold, they were otherwise uninjured, except Ruth Hindman had a ruptured eardrum. I went into headquarters today and got all the above from Bill Sheriden, our executive officer. I feel terrible about Johnny. Curiously enough, it was that infected finger that killed him. If he hadn't had this infected finger, he would have been up here with us, or maybe his number was just up. We have all been very lucky so far, as a matter of fact, and the wonder is that casualties in our outfit have not occurred before.

January 28, 1944—Horseshoe Bend on Mount Lungo

I had the graveyard shift today, from 4:00 P.M. until 8:00 A.M., and got by without a single case, believe it or not. The Thirty-sixth Division is doing practically nothing; in fact, we hear they are putting up defensive wire. The Thirty-fourth Division and the French are putting on a push north of us over Mount Sammucro, judging from the artillery sounding off in that direction. We went down to the Eleventh Field Headquarters and had a nice shower this P.M. After returning, Jerry dropped a few shells on Mount Rotundo behind us, which caused Trogh, Charlie, and me to dive into the shallow foxholes that we had dug. That character, Lyman Brewer, serving his first tour of duty in a field hospital, came running up all agog and fluttery, shouting, "What shall I do? What must I do?" Looking up from my foxhole, I said, "You had better find you a hole!" "But I don't have one!" he desperately moaned. Then, as an afterthought, with a brightening of his countenance, he exclaimed, "Well, do you mind if I lie down by your foxhole? If something happens to me, I want to be in good company!" He is some kind of character, all right, and a swell fellow. He does all his ward work from about midnight to 5:00 A.M. He is working on some sort of hand-powered positive pressure machine for chest cases.

January 29, 1944—Eleventh Field Hospital, on Horseshoe Bend
Charlie Westerfield has been viewing this antiaircraft observation post (AAOP) up on top of Mount Lungo to the northwest of us, and this afternoon we decided to go up there and get some pictures. We started up, inquiring about mines, were told that none had been found so far, so we proceeded. The hill is about a thousand feet high and quite steep. This was the hill that the Italians tried to take in the middle of December and where they were severely mauled, as would be expected. Since then, the Italians have been serving as muleskinners et cetera, which is what they are capable of. No wonder the Jerries were glad to get rid of them. The boys at the AAOP said that the Italians claimed they ran out of ammunition, but these boys had found all kind of Eyetie arms and ammunition scattered over the hill. In fact, they had collected a bunch of Italian rifles and cartridges and were firing the rifles for the fun of it to help pass the time. We arrived at the OP considerably winded and weary, having investigated a Jerry antitank gun and three machine-gun emplacements half way up the hill. The emplacements could not be detected for more than fifty yards and were holes dug into the rocks, roofed over the top with railroad ties, and covered completely with rocks. Only a direct hit could have done much harm, and apparently two of the dugouts had suffered just that. I believe a shell had hit on every square yard of this hill; the shell fragments and duds were all over the place. Most of the duds were Jerry 88s; we only saw two of our 155 mm. duds. We took the boys pictures with Summacro as a background. They had been photographed yesterday by a *Life* photographer. They live up there constantly, having supplies hand carried up to them daily. They are pretty well fixed, as a matter of fact. Their equipment consists of captured Jerry spotting scope, a short-wave sending and receiving set, and a telephone. We bulled with them, watched the front line smoke over along the Rapido, looked at planes through the spotting scope, shot numerous rounds of Jerry and Eyetie rifles, and, all in all, had a good time. Colonel Forsee is spending the night here and spent a lot of time in our tent shooting the breeze.

January 30, 1944—Eleventh Field Hospital, Horseshoe Bend on Mount Lungo
Nothing much happened today. A lot of big shots, including General

January 29, 1944—Charlie Westerfield and I inspect a typical German antitank gun emplacement on Mount Lungo overlooking the Mignano gap.

Blesse, Colonel Martin, et cetera, were here and I had to make rounds with them. Trogh and Charlie have started foxholing one corner of our tent, and I helped them a little.

January 31, 1944—Horseshoe Bend on Mount Lungo

Had a tedious case last night, a phosphorus shell wound with severe burns. It took almost four hours to do him. Today, Charlie and I deepened the foxhole, carving three seats and a center table, which is covered with a blanket and equipped with candles and a deck of cards and score pad. We all three can get into it quite comfortably. The foxhole is covered with some stray planks we found, and our personal boxes are on top of them. Not many casualties coming in, although I was told to be ready for a lot tonight. This afternoon Charlie, Gordon, Paul, and I got in a borrowed Jeep and drove down the road investigating (1) a German defense trench, (2) an unexploded bomb near the trench, (3) a beat-up United States tank named "Barbara" that had run into a 900-pound TNT booby trap, (4) Mignano, and (5) San Pietro-in-Fine. Mignano is the darnedest pile of rubble I have ever seen, and San Pietro is almost as bad.

January 31, 1944—Remains of Mignano, Italy, after bombings and shellings.

January 1944—Approaches to Cassino from top of Mount Lungo. Foreground—Mount Porchia; middle—Mount Trocchio; rear—Mount Cassino. Arrow points to town of Cassino.

View of San Pietro-in-Fine nestled under Mount Sammmuero. Scene of severe fighting, taken from Horseshoe Bend on Highway 6 on Mount Lungo, January 1944.

February 1, 1944—Horseshoe Bend on Mount Lungo, Eleventh Field Hospital

We awakened late as usual. Floyd Jergensen, the gas gangrene specialist, came up after lunch, and we went around and around about "Eddie" (Oedematians, a form of gas infection) as usual. Finally, Henry Hoffman, Gordon Madding, and I piled in Jergy's jeep and went tearing back to the Eleventh Evac to see a case of alleged "Eddie," which appeared to me to be a peritonitis. Jergy calls me a hard-headed Dutchman, which I consider the pot calling the kettle black. We got back about dark, and there in our tent was Major Stewart with two bottles of excellent cognac. He had gotten orders to report as surgical consultant with the air corps, so he thought we would help him get rid of his breakables. So we helped him.

72

February 2, 1944—Horseshoe Bend on Mount Lungo, Eleventh Field Hospital

Not busy at all today. Werner Hoeflick (Lyman Brewer's team) had a birthday today, and his team threw a party with wine, canapes, and, of course, the Yocky-Docky, which I undertook to mix properly from my vast experience. Miss Thomas, Lyman Brewer's nurse, thought it was lemonade, and although I warned her, she got pretty well lit. We sang some songs, and broke up about 10:00 P.M.

February 3, 1944—Eleventh Field Hospital, Mount Lungo

General Blesse made rounds today and was quite pleased with our work. We really had a lot of belly cases for him to look over. This P.M. Charlie, Paul Kennedy, and I went up to another peak of Mount Lungo and looked over a seventy-five caliber antitank gun, a bunch of Jerry dugouts, pillboxes, et cetera. There was a lot of equipment Jerry and the Italians had left, all of which we treated circumspectly.

Just another Kraut (Geechee Wolff) in a shot-up helmet, Mount Lungo, February 3, 1944.

73

February 4, 1944—Horseshoe Bend on Mount Lungo

We are still not very busy at this hospital, but to the north of us, the Thirty-fourth Division and the French have been attacking Cassino for three or four days now, and the artillery is rumbling, barking, cracking, and blasting almost constantly. It is claimed that we are in Cassino now, but Jerry is not taking it lying down. About 11:00 A.M., shells began to whistle over us, a regular duel. Tonight at 11:00 P.M., we had a bunch of shells, which screamed just overhead and hit the valley back of us. The first one was enough for me. I dived into our foxhole, carrying the hand of gin rummy I was playing with Trogh. He brought the rest of the cards, and we finished the game in the hole, under candlelight but very comfy. We are very happy to have our deluxe foxhole all fixed up comfortable and clean. The three of us can sit in it quite nicely. There is a flurry of digging about the camp tonight, in spite of its raining to beat the band.

February 5, 1944—Horseshoe Bend on Mount Lungo

Charlie Westerfield and I went up on Mount Lungo again this afternoon, taking the boys at the antiaircraft OP some fudge we had Francis Mosher mix up for them. The atmosphere was unbelievably clear, and there was enough wind to blow the smoke away from the front lines. We made our way well forward to where we could observe things clearly. We had a fine time; the whole battlefield was spread out below us like a huge map. The Liri River, the Rapido River, and their junction to form the Garigliano looked like silver ribbons. On our right, Mount Cairo loomed up behind Cassino, the town itself being cut off from our view by Mount Trocchio. However, the Abbey of Cassino, a huge building, was plainly visible. Twenty-four of our B-26s went directly overhead and dropped their bombs on a Jerry position behind a ridge, and we could see the brownish smoke mushroom up. After a while, two of our A-36s came up and dive-bombed the same positions. There were three of our Grasshopper (Cub planes) floating around over the German lines all afternoon. These pigmy planes must really aggravate the Germans. They look so helpless, but are always right there. The opposing antiaircraft boys don't dare shoot at them for fear of giving their positions away and having a deluge of artillery shells about their ears. There were a couple of batteries of Jerry big guns along the base of the mountains across the river, which would cut loose every once in a while. The hollow booms could be very distinctly heard, followed by the whistling of the shells across the valley, and then the explosion and c-r-u-m-p of the shells bursting on a ridge north of the monastery. The Germans also shelled a bunch of houses to the northeast of Cassino very vigorously for a while. Of course, our guns were firing a lot, too, and their flashes could be seen all over the place. Our artillery was using a lot of phosphorus shells, and these burst stood out like sore thumbs whenever they hit. About the time we got back to the OP, eight F.W. 190s came dashing in from the northwest over the Cassino area, and believe me, they got a warm welcome. Our A.A. boys really gave it to them. Three kept on coming and went over Mount Sammucro, when one of the planes developed an acute case of incendiarism, and down he came. Our A.A. shells were bursting right in the middle of them all the way, and I'll bet those pilots were really scared. The ack-ack the Jerries threw up on our B-26s was negligible compared to what we threw up to those sneak raiders. The only trouble was that we were right on top of this peak and when some guy hit the top of it near us with a 20 mm. ack-ack shell, we lost interest in watching and dived into one of the boy's dugouts. All in all, it was a most interesting afternoon.

February 6, 1944—Eleventh Field Hospital, Horseshoe Bend on Mount Lungo

They brought in a fellow from over at San Pietro who had really been hit by a Jerry shell. He died before we could get him started. He had photos of the nicest-looking girl, his wife, and year-old daughter in his pockets. This sort of thing sickens me. Also, Captain Markowicz, attached to the Thirty-sixth Division Clearing Station just across the road from us, was killed on his way up to a collecting company this afternoon. He had often been across the street to visit us.

February 8, 1944—Eleventh Field Hospital, Horseshoe Bend on Mount Lungo

What another night! It rained all afternoon, but our tent remained dry except for the foxhole, which gradually filled up from seepage. At about 4:00 A.M., Trogh yelled to Charlie and me to wake up. We did and turned on our flashlights. There was a river running in our front door, and water was six inches deep in our tent. Our trash can and water bucket looked very comical drifting majestically across the tent. There was nothing to do except to lie there and giggle about the whole situation, which we did. At about 7:30 A.M., our strong right arm, Scotty, came sloshing through this lake to check up on his guys. We welcomed him with shouts and laughter. He sloshed around trying to straighten things up a bit, retrieving floating effects as best he could. Unfortunately, we all forgot about our fancy deep foxhole, which, of course, was part of the lake. Scotty wandered over into that corner and suddenly found himself standing in water up to his umbilicus, ice water at that. Lying there in our nice, warm sacks, we laughed so hard that tears streamed down our faces! Poor Scotty got to laughing, too, and being unable to get any wetter, he went out, found a shovel, and dug a ditch through the dam that some dopes had built in trenching a ward tent. This allowed us to get up without wading, but mud and wet clothes still with us everywhere!

February 10, 1944—Eleventh Field Hospital, Horseshoe Bend on Mount Lungo

Charlie and I went back to Headquarters to get some things. It was a frightfully cold ride, and we accomplished practically nothing, as usual. We did get some letters, which made the trip worthwhile. Every time I go to that damn post exchange at Caserta, I get sore. One apparently has to be dressed up in pinks and a blouse and have a card before they will let you buy anything. Those of us up forward aren't able to get anything anywhere. We got back in the afternoon and immediately started to work operating finishing up about midnight. I had one swell case, a transdiaphragmatic splenectomy that came off like cases should come off.

February 11, 1944

Not too busy today. There are masses of New Zealanders and Indians moving up, and it is reported that the Thirty-sixth and Thirty-fourth Divisions are to be pulled out. I let Trogh do a nice case, liver and chest, which we approached in a somewhat unorthodox manner. We are getting so we will attempt almost anything. In fact, we have to.

February 12, 1944—Eleventh Field Hospital, Horseshoe Bend on Mount Lungo

Just when things seem on the point of quieting down nicely, Jerry starts his troubles again. About 5:00 A.M. the old screech and crash started in, the shells coming in from the direction of Cassino, passing over us, and landing in the valley back toward Mignano. Some of them were short and hit on the side of Mount Lungo, showering pebbles down on us. I was called to see a case that was frightfully shot up and in desperate shock. Finally, day broke and the Piper cubs went out looking, but still Jerry kept them coming in. We started operating after breakfast and finished about noon. The shelling stopped about 10:00 A.M.

The news came about the wiping out of Darby's Rangers at Cisterna up at Anzio. It is generally agreed that General Lucas, the commanding general at Anzio, was much too cautious. He could have sent his Rangers into Cisterna on D day with hardly a shot being fired at them, but he waited for four or five days before sending them in. They met an entire division with many tanks and were completely surrounded and had to surrender.

February 13, 1944—Eleventh Field Hospital, Horseshoe Bend on Mount Lungo

We got word that one of our nurses, "Tex" Farquahar, was killed outright at Anzio by a shell, and that Phil Giddings and Tony Emmi were wounded, the former with a through-and-through wound of the buttocks and colon and the latter with a fragment wound in the face. Four shells hit right in the middle of the Thirty-third Field Hospital area. Two of our enlisted men were wounded, also. This sort of thing is very depressing, particularly when the same thing might happen right here at any moment. We got our first Indian casualty in today. Tonight, Charlie and I went across the road to the Thirty-sixth Division Clearing Station and saw a movie just after dark, *Above Suspicion*. The flickering and noise from the artillery were not too disturbing.

February 14, 1944—Eleventh Field Hospital, Mount Lungo

The infantry boys that come in wounded tell us they are taking a terrific beating trying to save the monastery at Cassino, and it makes everyone angry that the big boys insist on saving this building. We simply have got to get over this sentimental, fair-play, save-the-building attitude. The sacrifice is far too great. *In retrospect, I can see it was a grave error to destroy the monastery. Its destruction really was very advantageous to the Germans, and grave political repercussions with the entire world ensued from our destroying the monastery. I suppose I was unduly influenced by talking to the wounded GIs, who were universally in favor of knocking down the monastery.*

February 15, 1944—Mount Lungo

A sight to gladden the eyes today. Seventy-two B-17s came over about 9:00 A.M., very high, and knocked the monastery down. There were over 100 B-25s and B-26s, which bombed this same area while some A-36s finished it off. Boy! was that something to watch. It should have been done a month ago, though. It is said that 200 Germans ran out of the building after the first bombing run and our artillery really let them have it. Jerry is still throwing shells into the area just over the hill, though. Another terrifically wounded case today, which I operated on, but I am afraid there is no chance for his survival. I am beginning to feel all is futile.

February 16, 1944—Eleventh Field Hospital, Horseshoe Bend on Mount Lungo

Colonel Forsee came up for no reason that I could detect, except to tell us that we would be called back to Headquarters soon. The Eleventh Field Hospital is to be set up as a station hospital for the Thirty-fourth and Thirty-sixth Division when they are pulled back. I did four postmortems this afternoon on my patients. The other boys are referring to my team as "Fatal 15." I have never seen such a run of lousy cases; it takes from three to four hours to do them, and then they die. It isn't funny.

February 18, 1944—Horseshoe Bend on Mount Lungo

"Fatal 15" still functioning. A case of abdominal gas infection was encountered today, and I was glad to be able to show it to Major Stewart. The picture is very characteristic. Still alive, but won't be tomorrow.

February 19, 1944—Horseshoe Bend on Mount Lungo

Maybe our luck will change. Two cases today that should get along okay. Things are going poorly everywhere. The news from Anzio is bad. They pulled Sullivan away from us yesterday and sent him to Anzio today. The Indians captured the monastery and railroad station at Cassino, but were promptly chased out again. A tank attack was scheduled across the Rapido north of Cassino, but Jerry got sixteen direct hits on the bridge they had put across the flooded area, and that was that.

February 22, 1944—Eleventh Field Hospital, Horseshoe Bend on Mount Lungo

A bit warmer today. We heard that a shell had landed there between the tents of Hopkins and Bos up at Anzio, demolishing the tents. Fortunately, everyone was in surgery so that no one was injured. I expect we will be sent up there before long. Had another case of gas gangrene infection, the upper extremity this time. I had to dissect out a lot of the shoulder girdle muscles, a tedious job.

February 26, 1944—Eleventh Field Hospital, Horseshoe Bend on Mount Lungo

We are evacuating patients rapidly, or else they are all dying. We are getting ready to fold up. Tonight a curious thing happened. Almost everyone was in our tent having a little Yocky-Docky when about 9:30 P.M., the center pole began to shake and everything began to rattle. The ground, which is mostly rock here, felt as if it had become semifluid and unstable. For an instant we couldn't figure out what happened; then someone said, "Earthquake!" It was really a very sharp quake and lasted possibly five seconds. There were several minor quakes later. The most striking sensation it gave me was that I was standing on a squashy bog, even though we were on almost a solid rock.

February 28, 1944—Eleventh Field Hospital, Horseshoe Bend on Mount Lungo

One year ago today we pulled out of New York Harbor aboard the *Andes.* I have seen a lot and done a lot but I still have a feeling of futility and sadness about the year. I much prefer the normal humdrum life in the United States with the wife and kids. Today Henry Hoffman and Gordon Madding's teams pulled out and we are left here with two patients who, as soon as they are able to be evacuated, will move out.

February 29, 1944—Eleventh Field Hospital, Mount Lungo

A Mr. Lee McCardell, foreign correspondent for the *Baltimore Sun,* looked me up today at my brother Miles's request. McCardell seems like a nice fellow, and as we had nothing to do, we asked him to spend the night, which he did. This afternoon, we piled into an ambulance and went back for a hot shower at the Fifth Army processing plant, a real assembly line for getting clean. One can trade one's clothes in for clean clothes, and one is forced to go through six hot showers, which was wonderful. Mac went with us. We came back, had supper, and sat around the stove shooting the breeze and drinking Yocky-Docky until about 11:00 P.M. Then we started frying a chicken Sergeant Smith of the Twelve Medical Depot across the road had brought over to us in appreciation for letting him watch some operations. Charlie Westerfield fried it, and it was honestly the best chicken I have tasted since I left home. The wonder of it is, it was the first chicken Charlie had ever fried. We broke up the party about 1:30 A.M.

March 1, 1944—Eleventh Field Hospital, Mount Lungo

McCardell came over about 9:00 A.M., and we had coffee, toast, and jam. He had to leave then. The subsequent account of this visit appears in the index. I believe he enjoyed his visit. This evening, Colonel Forsee showed up and told us we were going into the Tenth Field Hospital, which is backing up the Eighty-eighth Division over on the Garigliano to our left. We have to get back to Headquarters tomorrow and go back to work Friday. Got paid today by Tom Ballentine, but this invasion "wallpaper" with which we are paid has very little resemblance to real money.

My team, Eleventh Field Hospital, Horseshoe Bend, Mount Lungo, February 29, 1944. Left to right: Capt. Trogler Adkins, Durham, North Carolina, Capt. Chas. Westerfield, Savannah, Georgia and Maj. Luther Wolff, Columbus, Georgia. Taken by Baltimore Sun correspondent McCardell.

March 2, 1944—Headquarters

We left the Eleventh Field Hospital platoon this morning and came by Eleventh Field Headquarters at Piedemonte d'Alife. We saw a good many of our old friends there. We even chiselled a Coca-Cola, which are to be rationed now, three a week. It was the first Coke I have had in over a year now. It sure tasted good. Arrived at headquarters about 5:00 P.M., went up and talked things over with Colonel Forsee. I am still to be stuck in the job of chief of surgical service, damn it! Gordon, with Paul Kennedy and Bill Weiss; Hugh Swingle with George Flynn and Jimmy Dry; Tom Ballentine with Sydoriak and Buddy Hart are the other teams. Ballentine and Swingle haven't worked in a field hospital yet, we will have a bit of coaching to do, and I am very glad that Gordon Madding is along, because I know he can get the work done, and right.

March 3, 1944—Tenth Field Hospital, near Carano, Italy

Our "convoy" of one command car, five six-by-six trucks, and one weapons carrier pulled out at 9:00 A.M. and slowly proceeded up Highway 7 to the site near Carano. We arrived about 11:30 A.M. in a driving rain and a sea of mud. Maj. Ralph Plyler, from Salisbury, North Carolina, is in command of this platoon, and he was considerably distraught. All his vehicles were stuck in the mud, the engineers were trying to build a road into the hospital, the hospital was only just beginning to be set up, and everything was a mess. We had to lug all of our equipment and tents about 200 yards and set them up. We are supposed to start taking patients about 2:00 P.M., but none came in, thank God. We got squared away okay, although damp and muddy.

March 4, 1944—Tenth Field Hospital, Carano, Italy
A steady rain all last night and today. Hugh Swingle came in early this morning, declaring that he had had enough of this life. He had developed diarrhea during the night, soiled his pants, had taken a couple of trips through the mud and rain to the uncovered latrine, and developed a nosebleed; all in all, he had had a miserable night. He declared that he was no field soldier. I told him I would take his calls and he could rest up and see how he felt in a few days. By night, he had recovered pretty well. This area is getting muddier and muddier by the minute. This sector is the quietest and most free from danger of shelling than any we have been in since back on the Volturno. We are about three miles from the sea, which is to the west of us. The mountains across the Garigliano are about five to seven miles north of us, and no military installations are near us. Our artillery is well ahead of us for a change; I believe the closest gun is a good mile or two away. We still have no patients although we are ready. Trogh, Charlie, and Tom went up to the Ninety-fourth Evac to get us some floor boards today. Our tarp is just too wet and muddy to use.

March 5, 1944—Tenth Field Hospital, Carano, Italy
It rained all day today, and the mud is fierce. Colonel Forsee and Paul ("Buck") Samson came up today to see how we were getting along. The Eighty-eighth Division has moved one regiment into the line last night. Quite a few casualties through this clearing station this morning. Our floor boards are swell. Had ice cream tonight, first I have had since Africa.

March 7, 1944—Tenth Field Hospital, Carano, Italy
It being a nice day, Paul Kennedy, "The General," and I walked into Carano this morning. There are a lot of quaint and fascinating sights and vistas in these little towns if you ignore the dirt, the odors, et cetera. We went here and there asking for eggs, finally collecting one dozen, at twenty cents an egg. Tonight we had a big egg fry in our

81

tent, with the old maestro at the frying pan. There were no adverse comments, so I guess I fried them okay. Today is my wife's birthday. It is no fun.

March 9, 1944—Tenth Field Hospital, Carano, Italy
This evening, Charlie, Tom Ballentine, and I got hold of a jeep and rode down to the sea, which looks a couple of miles away, but actually is about six by road. This morning we went back to Headquarters, ostensibly to attend a meeting, but actually to get a generator. I was flabbergasted when the old man readily agreed. Tonight, we have a light and a radio going instead of the usual candlelight, and does it help!

March 10, 1944
Charlie Westerfield shaved off his mustache today, all due to the evil influence of a woman. We now call this female Delilah, although she refuses to answer to this name. Trogh and I have been riding the two of them unmercifully.

March 11, 1944—Tenth Field Hospital, Carano, Italy
The boys want to hang a sign on the morgue tent here: "Surgery-G.S. #6." Gordon Madding's team is known as Surgical Team Number Six, and he surely has had tough luck with his patients lately. I ordered the boys not to put up the sign.

March 13, 1944—Tenth Field Hospital, Carano, Italy
Today is a nice springlike day, but last night the tent pretty nearly blew down. A cold wind from the northeast flopped and banged things all night long. Charlie said he didn't get to sleep before 4:00 A.M. I got awakened at 2:30 A.M. by Swingle wanting to borrow our ax. I was kept awake then by the loud shouts and poundings as they secured their tent, which was about to blow down. Anyhow, I had to get up and do a case about that time, so it didn't make much difference.

March 14, 1944—Tenth Field Hospital, Carano, Italy
It rained like the devil during the night again, but today is another nice spring day. We had our first belly case in this location this A.M., which I let Trogh do. Not too extensively injured and in good shape, although thirty-six hours post wounding. Trogh, Charlie, and I were planning to go into Naples at 3:30 and had gotten all bathed and shaved when Colonel Forsee showed up, without the mail. We found that he was planning to spend the night, so our trip was cancelled pronto. I haven't any idea why he has come up or why he decided to stay so

Carano, Italy—Officers watch bombing of Cassino, March 15, 1944.

long. He got a phone call telling him that the orders on Bill Weiss had come through transferring him home on this rotation basis business. That is swell for Bill, and Al Shure is also going home. I suppose any break like this for me is utterly hopeless.

March 15, 1944—Tenth Field Hospital, Carano, Italy
This morning our air force really did a job. Beginning about 9:00 A.M., wave after wave of B-17s, B-24s, and B-26s sailed over Cassino and really let them have it. They usually came in from the east over the target, dropped their bombs, and then turned south, passing close overhead. It was a tremendous sight. The rumble and jar of the bombs could be felt very plainly here, some fifteen miles away. I think at least 400 bombers went over, besides plenty of escorting fighters. The last flight went over just before noon. We heard over the radio tonight that 28,000 tons of bombs had been unloosed on the Cassino area, and then the infantry attacked. The radio said this was the greatest weight of bombs ever dropped on a target in the Mediterranean area. We have heard rumors that this bombing was to take place for weeks, but the

83

weather has been too lousy to carry it out. This afternoon we saw a very curious and inexplicable phenomenon. Bands of light and shadow raced across the sky from north to south. There appeared to be three suns, set in a complete circle of vapor or high clouds. No one could figure it out. A veritable cloudburst started about sundown and continued through the night. *We heard later that the infantry attack on Cassino failed, mostly because of this terrible cloudburst.*

March 16, 1944—Tenth Field Hospital, Carano, Italy
Nothing much doing today. "Sig" Sanzen and Charlie Rife were over this P.M. visiting. Shortly after supper a crap game started in our tent. It was impossible to write or read, so finally I got so disgusted I got in for a bit. Managed to break even by 11:30 P.M., when the lights went out and Charlie and I went to bed. However, Buddy Hart, Trogh, and Berlin still were on the floor rolling the dice by candlelight, which they continued to do until 7:15 A.M., the damn fools.

March 21, 1944
Another quiet day. This is the easiest time we have had since D day at Salerno. Played a little fungo with Paul Kennedy and George Flynn this afternoon. This Tenth Field Hospital outfit is getting a little too interested in our affairs to suit me. As far as I am concerned, what our bunch does during the hours off is their own affair as long as they behave themselves and take good care of their patients. Oh, well, maybe things will iron out by themselves.

March 27, 1944—Carano, Italy
Still nothing much doing. It rained and was cold. The attack on Cassino has about petered out, with no progress in spite of tremendous bombings, artillery barrages, and loss of lots of lives. The Germans are probably the best soldiers in the world.

March 29, 1944
We were all off duty today. After lunch, Trogh, Charlie, Berlin, and I got in Berlin's jeep, went over to the showers, and then on into Naples to view Mount Vesuvius, which has been blowing its top for the last couple of weeks. From the Autostrada one obtained a magnificient view, heavy brownish smoke boiling and rolling up for thousands of feet from the summit. The whole mountain is covered with light gray ash that makes it appear snow-covered. The lava flow is a big black streak running down the northwest side of the mountain, and the distance it flowed is simply unbelievable. We knew that the villges of San Sebastian and Somma di Massa had been pretty well destroyed,

and we decided to go over there and have a look. We spent about two hours trying to find the roads to these villages and finally got straightened out. We thought we could go from Somma to San Sebastian according to the map, and as we neared the former place, Trogh started yelling, "Show me the larva." The road was rough and we weren't looking ahead much, so that we darn near ran smack into this wall of lava about thirty feet high, which lay across the road in Somma. We stopped just in time and climbed out. The lava had cooled enough to climb up on it, although stinking smoke and vapors still poured out of various crevices. I must say it was an amazing sight. The flow was about thirty feet deep, quarter of a mile wide, and extended about half a mile beyond Somma, fully five miles from the crater. It swept everything before it, houses, churches, trees, everything. It was incredible that it could have flowed so far. The whole thing looked like a vast clinker pile. Somma di Massa means "The End of the Flow." It was the end of the flow of some previous eruption, but this one fooled them and no longer is the name of the town applicable. Went back to Naples and up to the Orange Club, which is in a beautiful place on a wonderful site. We each had a few drinks and each ordered a complete dinner, plus extra desserts. Got caught in an air alert as we got out of Naples, but nothing much happened. We were certainly the country boys going to town; everyone was all dressed up at the Orange Club but us. We had our usual field clothes and felt conspicuous.

March 31, 1944—Tenth Field Hospital, Carano, Italy
Major Plyler, the CO of this outfit, whom we have nicknamed "Prune Face" and call him that to his face, has clamped down on our nurses' having dates in their tents. The nurses are sore as hell, especially at me. I had nothing whatsoever to do with it. Most women are inconceivably irrational. The Tenth field outfit can't understand the way all of us got along so well with each other in the Second Aux.

April 4, 1944—Tenth Field Hospital, Carano, Italy
Five more of our outfit were slightly wounded up at the Anzio beachhead, viz: Black Robbie, Hopkins, Bos, Shorbe, and Pappy Gay. It was a bomb this time. I guess it was miraculous that any of them escaped serious injury. Black Robbie and Hoppy were in their tents and foxholes. The bomb crater was present only four feet away, they say.

April 5, 1944—Tenth Field Hospital, Carano, Italy
A couple of patients came in this morning, and it was 6:00 P.M. before we finished them. Gordon had a boy with multiple wounds, including a spinal cord wound and neck wound. He got the fellow in

85

fair shape and started to give him an anesthetic when the patient coughed and blood flew three feet into the air from a severed carotid artery. Gordon grabbed a knife and cut down, but the guy died anyhow. General Martin was in the room at this time but somehow saw nothing amiss at all, even though I abruptly left him and got in to help Gordon.

April 10, 1944—Tenth Field Hospital, Carano, Italy

Today Charlie, Trogh, Scottie, Dunlap, and I piled into Frank Hall's jeep, which "The General" somehow obtained yesterday, and off we took for Naples to try to see *This Is the Army*, with music by Irving Berlin. We went down by the coast road through Mondragone. Trogh, the driver, thinks a jeep will fly. We managed to get tickets for the afternoon performance and decided to run back out to Marcianise to Headquarters and get the mail and eat lunch. We had a nice talk with Colonel Forsee. He is sending teams up to the beachhead on rotation. The boys up there are getting sort of frazzled! He said he was going to send one of our teams but not mine just yet. This is okay by me. We got caught in convoys going back to Naples and arrived at the San Carlo Opera House just as the show started. The seats were all occupied, so Trogh and I wandered into a box that was marked "Private" but only contained two people in eight seats. A British captain came in, slightly drunk and highly indignant. "This is my private box!" he screamed. "We are sorry," I said. "But just how does one arrange for a private box?" Well, he kept talking about its being an American show et cetera which I didn't follow at all. Finally he called an usher and told him to find us seats. We said okay. "You Americans drive me wild!" he cried. I didn't see what all this commotion was about, so I replied, "That's right; you are wild." "Yes," he agreed. "I am wild." This sort of inane conversation kept going until he found us a box reserved for the British. I don't know why the British seem to think they are the conquering heroes of this country and are entitled to all privileges.

The show was good, but it was not the army, and not entirely up to expectations. Irving Berlin looks much younger than I anticipated. After the show we decided to get a few drinks, so Trogh insisted on going to the "Turistico," the nurses' hotel, to see if he knew anyone there. He found two of our nurses, Annie Smith and Miss Neubert, registered, so he called them down and got us all in the bar. We had a few rounds of this and that, ate dinner, and came on home after picking up Scottie and Dunlap at the MP headquarters. A car (limousine), license-number U.S.A. 6401, was in front of us and kept driving very foolishly, and every time we started to pass it, he would speed up and prevent it. I got sore and told Trogh to pull up and stop him. This he did. I got out and said to the driver, "What kind of damn fool driving is this?" I then saw the eagles on his shoulders. He was one of the air corps youngsters and looked about thirty years old. I had gone too far to back down by then, so I bawled him out for about five minutes. He never recovered at all, fortunately, and although he started up ahead of us, he soon pulled off to the side of the road and that's the last time I saw him. He was probably pretty drunk, or he would never have let me get away with a mere major chewing out a bird colonel.

April 13, 1944—Carano, Italy

Hugh Swingle did some fast talking about his "research" to keep from going to Anzio. Hugh is one of my confrers from the Mayo Clinic. He finished there about two years after I did. He is more like a fastidious old maid than anything else and really hates the life in the field with its dirt, mud, and inconveniences. He has had more than his share of abdominal wound separations "dehiscences," and I showed him how to close the abdomen with through-and-through sutures tied laterally over rubber tubes to close the dehiscences. Hugh had had much more than his share of abdominal dehiscences simply because he grossly oversews the wounds, putting his sutures about a milimeter apart and thoroughly strangulating the tissue. Anyhow, he persuaded the colonel that his research was quite necessary and therefore didn't get to go to Anzio.

April 16, 1944—Tenth Field Hospital, Carano, Italy

Ruth Hindman and Miss Carlyle, who were subbing for our Sorrento vacationing nurses, had to go back today, so we threw a little farewell party for them last night. Paul Kennedy taught Charlie and me a vaudeville routine called "Dapper Dan," and we performed it to many encores. We also had an "inchie-pinchie," game which pretty nearly busted some of the boys' and girls' insides from laughing. The goats were Hindman and Stratton. A very hilarious evening.

April 18, 1944—Tenth Field Hospital, Carano, Italy

Charles, Trogh, and I went down to Naples to see an opera—at least Charles and I did, while Trogh visited a friend in the 300th General Hospital. The 300th General Hospital is in a magnificient building high on a hill above Naples. It is truly a swell layout. Charlie and I saw *La Boheme* at the San Carlo Opera House. It was very good, and the scenes were most elaborate. The girls' parts were taken by typical fat, buxom singers, especially that of Mimi. This always seems quite incongruous, as Mimi is supposed to be dying of chronic tuberculosis. I enjoyed the opera immensely, however. After the show, we picked Trogh up at the 300th General Hospital and went, after several unintentional deviations, to the Orange Club for dinner. We saw Tom Burford and our head nurse, Miss Price, there. The latter was being deluged with Canadians. I got to talking to a kilt-clad Canadian and asked him what he wore under his skirt. He said, "Nothing. If the colonel catches anyone in our outfit with underwear on, they have to buy drinks for all the officers in the outfit." This seemed improbable, but he acted very serious.

April 26, 1944—Carano, Italy, Tenth Field Hospital
It started with a cloudburst about 2:00 A.M., and it has poured all day. John, a Italian boy working here for his keep, insists, "Alla time nica day, now."

April 30, 1944—Carano, Italy, Tenth Field Hospital
I was dead tired tonight for no particular reason, and just as I was drifting off to sleep, I got called over to the admission tent. Three guys in, shot up all over and all three requiring amputations. I did two thigh amputations on two people with almost identical wounds. The whole popliteal area was torn away. I was really dead tired when it was all over.

May 3, 1944—Tenth Field Hospital, near Carano, Italy
Gordon got the business today. He is to go back to Headquarters tomorrow or the next day and off to Anzio. Sure hate to see him leave! Also hate to see the "Little General," Paul Kennedy, go.

May 4, 1944—Tenth Field Hospital
There was a big blowout at Headquarters tonight, so we piled into an ambulance and went down in our field clothes. All the big shots were there for miles around, including General Martin. They were all dressed up, and we looked a little conspicuous in our field clothes. I got four swell letters from my wife, the high spot of the evening. I enjoyed seeing all my friends but danced very little. The drinks were most God-awful, a horrendous mixture of gin, anisette, and cognac.

May 6, 1944—Tenth Field Hospital, Carano
Howard Bos came up today to replace Gordon. This evening, Colonel Forsee called and told me to get packed up, Anzio-bound, it seems. Oh, well, I am sort of glad he is sending me. I am getting pretty well fed up with these birds coming back from Anzio screaming about how

hard it is up there when most of them never heard guns fire or shells burst before a couple of months ago. There have developed two cliques back at headquarters, the Anziites and non-Anziites. The former look down their noses at the latter. So, it is just as well to go on up and be able to say, "Yeah, I was there." We have been here so long that our possessions are scattered all over; packing and sorting are an ordeal.

Chapter II
Anzio to Rome

May 7, 1944—Aboard LST en route to Anzio

We hurriedly finished packing this A.M. and got loaded. At the last minute, Bill Nelson called and told us to go up by the Eleventh Field Hospital and pick up Weiss. He wasn't ready and we got entangled in some convoys, so that we arrived back at Headquarters just in time to grab a bite to eat, get the mail, see the colonel a few minutes, and get entrucked. We went by the Fifty-second Station Hospital and picked up Ken Lowry and his team. Boarded the LST (Land Ship Tank) No. 76 after transferring our chests and baggage to a couple of ammo trucks. We pulled out of the Fairgrounds Harbor just at dark. There was a church service on the upper deck, which I attended. The moon was just coming up, and Vesuvius, Capri, and the Bay of Naples were lovely. We stayed at the rail for a couple of hours until we passed between Ischia and Procida. I had a cabin berth, but Trogh, Charlie, and Paul Kennedy slept on deck on Charlie's and my air mattresses. These LSTs roll something fierce when it is rough like it was last night, so we didn't sleep very well. A routine General Quarters occurred at 5:00 A.M., and we went on deck to see what was up. Nothing was. After breakfast, Anzio and Nettuna came into sight, and we came in and beached. All very quiet and peaceful. The buildings in these two towns aren't really very beat up, being hit by nothing but shell fire. They were probably quite nice towns formerly.

May 8, 1944—Eleventh Evac, Anzio

We arrived at the Eleventh Evac, where we were assigned about 10:30 yesterday morning. Gordon Madding is assigned there also. Gordon was surprised and please to see us. This Eleventh Evac is reputed to be a good outfit. Lieutenant Colonel Wilson, the chief of surgery, and Lieutenant Colonel Tabor, are swell fellows, and we think we will get along well in this outfit. All the hospitals here are in one crowded area. There are six evac hospitals and the Thirty-third Field Hospital, which is being used as a four-hundred-and-fifty–bed evac. This area has been dubbed by the infantry as "Hell's Half Acre." I went over to the Thirty-third Field Hospital this P.M. Our guys are practically running this hospital. There have been a lot of improvements and changes since we were with them last October and November, because they were, without doubt, the lousiest hospital over here then. The teams of the Thirty-third are Jim Mason, Reeve Betts, Fred Jarvis, Herb Brinker, Henry Hoffman, Tom Ballentine, "Fish" Fishwick, and Frank Chunn. As is customary, there was much greeting, hullaballoo, and raucous chatter when different teams got together. Everyone here is well dug in, with sunken tents, sandbags, and sandbagged roofs over each cot. The operating rooms are timbered and sandbagged completely, so that one feels quite safe, for nothing but a direct hit can injure you.

May 9, 1944—Eleventh Evac Hospital, Anzio

Lyman Brewer showed up this A.M. to join Gordon and me here. I don't think we will work too hard. They are apparently going to give us mostly chests and bellies to do. This evening, Herb Brinker and I went for a walk for about two miles. There is actually not a good deal of evidence of war about, just a few bomb craters and a few shell holes.

May 10, 1944—Eleventh Evac Hospital, Anzio

We had a brisk air raid last night, although I heard no bombs drop, just a lot of antiaircraft. Jerry threw a few shells in over us and a couple about half a mile behind us. No work as yet. Everything quiet. Hugh Swingle came in this morning, assigned to the Thirty-third. I'm afraid he is in for a lot of rough riding among that bunch of guys. Jerry hit a large ammunition dump to the northwest of us this morning, quite a lot of smoke and explosions.

May 12, 1944—Eleventh Evac Hospital, Anzio

Herb Brinker is to go back to Headquarters in the A.M., Frank Hall replacing him. No work. Today we got our gin ration and threw a slight party in our tent, but since I was on, I didn't help out much. George Donaghy came over for our party. Felt like old times except for Johnny Adams being absent.

May 14, 1944—Eleventh Evac Hospital, Anzio

Today was Mother's Day, so I went to church. Spent the day reading and writing letters. Tonight three or four shells hit uncomfortably close, some shrapnel going through the Thirty-third's tents. These dugouts give me a remarkable sense of security. The report from the southern front really sounds good. The offensive in that area, which started on May 11, has progressed better than anticipated. Apparently we got away from that sector just in time to avoid an awful lot of work.

May 15, 1944—Anzio, Eleventh Evac Hospital

Tonight after supper we went over to the Thirty-third Field Hospital. The boys over there had picked up a small jackass somewhere and were playing around with it. Trogh and Frank Chunn had the idea of putting it in Swingle's tent, which they proceeded to do after a lot of pushing, pulling, and coaxing with candy. Swingle came back to his tent, looked in it, and refused to enter it, having nothing to do with it. The rest of us howled with laughter. Swingle just can't get used to the rough doings of this bunch of guys.

May 16, 1944—Eleventh Evac Hospital, Anzio

Today was "Cook's Tour" of the beachhead, courtesy of Sixth Corps. Charlie Westerfield, Frances Mosher, and I went with about fifteen officers and nurses to (1) Red Beach, (2) the airport, (3) Anzio and the Sixth Corps Museum, (4) the American cemetery, (5) the main A.A. battery on the beachhead, (6) the British Fourteenth Casualty Clearing Station, and (7) rose picking. The Third Division boys are down on Red Beach practicing mountain climbing, mine detection, et cetera. Red Beach is about two miles east of here. There were a lot of wrecked LCTs, LCVPs, and LCPs around and about on the beach. A Liberty ship is beached there also. While we were there, we saw the "Anzio Express" hit in the water but miss the ships by a wide margin. We finally got a good look close up of a Thunderbolt that was on the fighter strip. Some fighter plane! We then had a nice luncheon at the officers' mess in Anzio, followed by a visit to the Ordinance Museum, where most of the Jerry souvenirs are being collected, including sections of their 280 mm. shell (the "Anzio Express"). *The "Anzio Express" is a huge twelve-inch, long-range artillery railroad piece that is shuttled in and out of tunnels up in the Alban hills when our air force is absent because of darkness or inclement weather. This gun is curious in that each shell has tracks on it that fit rifling in the gun's barrel and is quite accurate. These shells make a very peculiar sound as they sail over.* The American cemetery fills one with a sense of futility and dread. Some 3,000 American youngsters are already buried there, besides about 1,500 Krauts. We saw the grave of "Tex" Farquhar, who was our nurse killed at the Thirty-third Field Hospital. We also saw Colonel Huddleston's grave. *Colonel Huddleston was a Surgeon of 2 Corps, then transferred to Anzio, becoming 6 Corps Surgeon. He was killed by a shell that hit Anzio. We called Colonel Huddleston "Col. Huddle-Fuddle," but he was a good man and very militarily oriented. It is said that he carried a .45 automatic on his hip at all times and when Jerry came over in an air raid on Anzio, he would go out in the street and fire this*

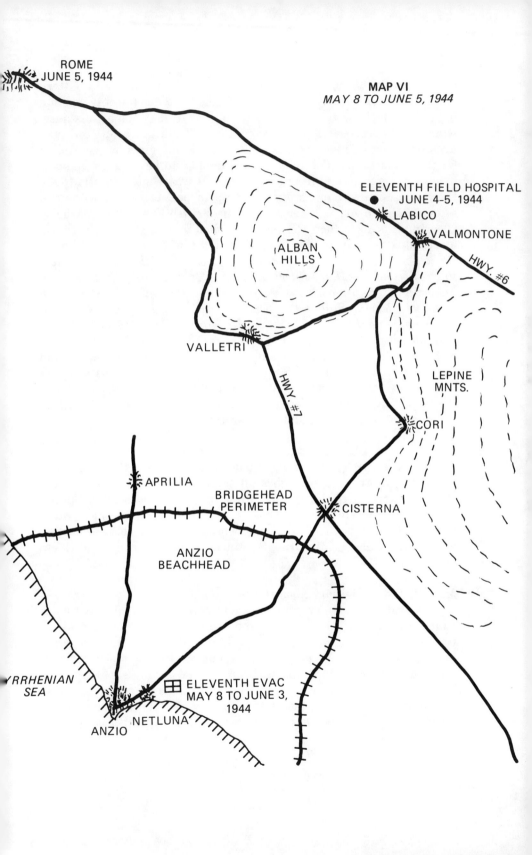

weapon at the high-flying German planes, futilely. The main battery of antiaircraft is simply amazing. They told us it was the only one like it in Europe. New type radar controls everything; height, distance, wind velocity, speed, temperature influence. These data are all collected and computed by machines, and all four 90 mm. guns are controlled by these machines. The only thing that has to be done by hand is loading the gun and pulling the lanyard. It was almost ghostly to see the four guns swinging around and up in perfect unison without a human being near. We then visited the British Fourteenth Casualty Clearing Station, where we were welcomed by Red Robertson, who is attached to this British outfit, and visited him for a couple of hours. *Red Robertson, of Paduckah, Kentucky, was one of the real characters in the Second Auxiliary Surgical Group. He has a very droll sense of humor and was a marvelous storyteller. The British of the Fourteenth Casualty Clearing Station had never seen nor heard anything like him, and he became their pet. They awarded him the British Empire Medal and later elected him to be an honorary member of the Royal College of Surgeons.* Red Robby gave us a double rye and tea and crumpets, and we had a fine visit. There are some beautiful rose gardens about in the fine residential sectors of Anzio, which are north of the main town. We helped the nurses collect armloads of these roses to carry back to the hospital. A pretty good day, all in all.

May 19, 1944—Eleventh Evac Hospital, Anzio
    Every day there is a rumor of a push starting from the beachhead, and certainly there is enough stuff to get one going. There are the Third, Thirty-fourth, Forty-fifth, First Armored, and a lot of Special Troops, and the Thirty-sixth Divison is on its way up, besides two or three British divisions. The boys down below on the coast sector are moving right along, Minturno, St. Maria Infante, Formia, and Gaeta are all cut off.

May 21, 1944—Eleventh Evac Hospital, Anzio
    Beautiful days and nights we are having. Italy has finally turned sunny and dry. Still nothing much doing except a nightly air raid or two, which don't amount to much. I think the A.A. boys are shooting just for the hell of it, for we rarely hear a plane. Jerry is pretty nervous, sending up flares almost constantly around the perimeter of the beachhead. The "Anzio Express" comes in a few rounds every night, but we have had nothing very close recently. All in all, this Anzio deal is not nearly as rough as last October, November, and December back in the Minturno Gap.

Hospital Center (called "Hell's Half-Acre" by GIs) near Nettuno, Anzio Beachhead, May 1944.

Anzio Beachhead, May 1944. Bedroom on the beachhead. Dirty and musty, but oh! so safe and relaxing.

May 22, 1944—Eleventh Evac, Anzio

The Thirty-sixth Division landed today, and it looks like things are about to break loose. The boys down below us keep right on coming and have Itra and Terracina cut off. A whole bunch of our teams are here now, mostly over at the Thirty-eighth Evac. I hardly know where they expect to use us all.

May 23, 1944—Eleventh Evac Hospital, Anzio

Everything looks all set for the push. We are all fed up with sitting around doing nothing. There was a tremendous barrage this morning at dawn, and the Third, Thirty-fourth, and Forty-fifth Divisions started a general push to cut off the German Tenth Army to the south. By 10:00 A.M., the casualties started rolling in, and by tonight the hospital is completely filled. Gordon started working this morning, as did Lyman Brewer. My team goes on at midnight, and there will be little rest for us for a while, I'm afraid. Lieutenant Colonel Wilson, chief of surgery, and Lieutenant Colonel Tabor, the CO told us to get some sleep today. It is pretty reliably reported that the Third has cut Highway 7 on both sides of Cisterna.

May 24, 1944—Eleventh Evac Hospital, Anzio

We are all practically dead with fatigue. Started in at midnight, worked until 11:00 A.M., got three hours' sleep, and started in again. It is now early morning, and we are still working, doing only the big cases, of which there is an inexhaustible supply. The casualties are very heavy; all the hospitals are filled to overflowing, and in our hospital there are two patients to an army cot in some of the lightly wounded wards. We are about 135 surgical cases behind. We are also getting a lot of Jerry casualties in. Cisterna has fallen and the boys are pushing on. We are seeing more bullet wounds than I have ever seen before. Snipers are everywhere, the boys say. Our infantrymen take very few prisoners.

May 25, 1944—Eleventh Evac Hospital, Anzio

Well, the beachhead is no more. The boys from the beachhead met the boys from down south at Borgio Groppa, about eight miles southeast of the bridgehead. The Eighty-eighth and Eighty-fifth Divisions have certainly done wonders in pushing this distance in so little time. I wouldn't have thought it possible. We hear that the boys have taken Cori and really have the Krauts on the run. The casualties are still very heavy, and every time I go on duty, my heart sinks on going ito the preoperative ward. It just doesn't seem that we will ever get caught up. Over a hundred patients behind still. I had to laugh today at one kid we were getting ready to operate on; he had a through-and-through right chest wound from a sniper's bullet and was in good shape. I asked him, "Isn't it pretty nerve-racking to make an attack against stuff like you had here?" "Well," he said, "you get pretty nervous before you jump off, but after you flush a few Jerries, it is just like hunting rabbits. Everybody is shooting and you don't pay much attention to it, because you don't know whether they are shooting at you or not." I don't know how these infantry boys do it.

May 26, 1944—Eleventh Evac Hospital, Anzio
We are still working eighteen to twenty hours a day, sleeping very badly in the afternoons, and we are getting punch-drunk, and tempers are getting pretty short. We are still doing mostly chest and bellies and don't have a lot of cases, but the ones we have are plenty tough. Not much news of advance today; so many of the boys don't know where geographically they were wounded, and their emergency medical tags are very indefinite. Most of our casualties are apparently from the vicinity of Cori. Quite a bit of transportation is coming up Highway 7 from the south. "Pruneface" Plyler dropped in today, and the Tenth Field Hospital is coming up tomorrow via trucks. Pruneface is still the same bull-slinger, but we enjoyed seeing him.

May 27, 1944—Eleventh Evac Hospital, Anzio
One day is practically like the next: worked eighteen hours, then slept four or five hours. One tends to lose track of dates and days. The infantry is fighting around Artena now, which the Jerries are trying to hold. Good progress on the whole. I hope I don't have to keep working nights indefinitely.

May 28, 1944—Eleventh Evac Hospital, Anzio
Started work last night after supper and worked straight through until 10:00 A.M. The boy on whom I did a transdiaphragmatic splenectomy and nephrectomy, as well as a kid from Concord, North Carolina (where I was born and reared), are both doing much better than they have any right to. The patient whose hepatic artery I was forced to tie off as well as suturing his liver and removing the gall bladder and suturing the duodenum is also doing well. The boys up front are not moving as fast today; I suppose they have to wait for supplies to catch up with them, but over in the Liri Valley the British, Canadians, and Indians are moving ahead against rear guard action only.

May 29, 1944—Eleventh Evac Hospital, Anzio

I have trouble remembering what day it is. One day is almost exactly like the next. We aren't eating properly because the midnight lunch is pretty lousy, and we often don't get dinner, requiring sleep more. Well, tomorrow Gordon is going on night shift and my team is going to start working days, so it shouldn't be so bad then. Frances Mosher broke down and started crying during an operation tonight so we had to send her off to bed. However, we went right on working. Our enlisted men, Scottie and Dunlap, are swell and really do a good job. Both are very dependable and never complain. Dunlap does make some very droll remarks, which keep us laughing a lot. The fall of Valmontone and Valletria seems imminent.

May 30, 1944—Eleventh Evac Hospital, Anzio

It is much nicer working days, and the casualties are slowing down a bit so that Gordon and I can go on· twelve-hour schedules, which beats eighteen hours or more very much indeed. Old Man "Pruneface" Plyler came by again and looked us up. It was good to see him, and he had the usual line of bull to throw. He still loves to be kidded, which we did unmercifully. The boys are pushing up on both sides of Valletria and are after Valmontone hot and heavy. All platoons of the Thirty-third Field Hospital have moved up beyond Cisterna, and the Tenth Field Hospital is slated to move up soon.

May 31, 1944—Eleventh Evac Hospital, Anzio

The war is moving on so far that except for the casualties still pouring in, and the distant northerly flickering of artillery, we wouldn't know a war was on. We still work as hard as possible, keeping quite busy on our twelve-hour shifts, but we see fewer bellies and chests than the first few days. The colonel dropped in to see us today, having driven up from the south. He looked tired and dusty. We were doing a kidney case at the time, so didn't get to talk to him much. He said headquarters was moving up soon. Colonel Tabor came around afterwards and told us what a swell job we had done and that he had told Colonel Forsee about it. A little flattery doesn't hurt, I guess. Valletria, one of the key points in the last line of defense before Rome, is virtually surrounded.

June 1, 1944—Eleventh Evac Hospital, Anzio

We are still plenty busy, but there isn't the sense of urgency that there has been. The Tenth Field Hospital has moved up toward Cori. Valletria and Valmontone have fallen, and the defense line has cracked wide open. Colonel Tabor keeps complimenting us on the work we have done. Lyman Brewer and his team of Schiff and Hoeflick are like a three-ring circus when they get going talking, and we are convulsed by their remarks. I wish I could record some of their conversations.

June 2, 1944—Eleventh Field Hospital, Anzio
We are still doing some pretty big stuff, but it is mostly rectal wounds, liver wounds, and patients that arrive after the long trip in pretty good shape. We had some good cold beer last night and are pretty well rested up, at least caught up on our sleep.

June 3, 1944—Eleventh Field Hospital, Anzio
(Three miles east of Cisterna.) Yesterday morning we were still about sixty cases behind. Today, we caught up and cleared out all the surgical cases. Just before noon when I was doing the last belly, Colonel Forsee walked in and I said, "Well, Colonel, we are all finished up here and ready to move on." He replied, "Well, that's fine, because I need some teams for a platoon of the Eleventh Field Hospital." So we said okay, but we need Gordon Madden to go with us. We argued quite a while about that. Well, after supper, Gordon and I went over to the advanced headquarters of the Second Aux. here at Anzio to argue some more but didn't because he said to take Gordon and get ready at once. He asked us to pick up Vince Iovine at the Fifteenth Evac and Ben Burbank at the Thirty-eighth Evac. We didn't get underway until dusk, but fortunately there was a brilliant moon and we could see quite well. All the houses (a Mussolini reclamation project) for miles on each side of the Mussolini Canal were just piles of rubble. Cisterna, which held out for a couple of days, was nothing but a heap of tumbled-down masonry also. We found two tents of the Eleventh Field Hospital near the Ninety-fifth Evac; the rest of the platoon had moved up. So we stayed in the Ninety-fifth Ward tent. I surely did miss my air mattress.

June 4, 1944—Eleventh Field Hospital, four miles northwest of Labico, Italy
This morning we got loaded and proceeded to our site to set up on Highway 6, four miles northwest of Labico. We went through Cori, Artena, and Valmontone, practically making a semicircle around the Alban Hills, or Colli Laziali, which is an old volcano with a large lake in its crater. It is said that Nero used to throw some real benders there. It is also the summer home of the pope. The road up through Cori passed through beautiful olive groves continuously, and from Cori to Valmontone the roadsides were littered with wrecked and burned out

Refugees on the road from Cori to Valmontone, June 3, 1944.

German vehicles, guns, half-tracks, tanks and self-propelled guns. The smell of decayed flesh from dead horses and men was terrific at times. Our air force, tanks, and artillery really caught them along this stretch, and the results were terrible for the Germans. I have never seen so much destroyed stuff anywhere. Valmontone was a shambles; about the only thing left standing was the cathedral. The ride was fearfully dusty, and everyone looked as if he were wearing a mask at the end of the ride. We got set up in a dusty wheat and corn field next to the Third Division Clearing Station at this site. Palestrina is just to the east of us and the Alban hills to the west. We started getting patients in about 4:00 P.M. from the outskirts of Rome, and right after supper we started to work, working straight through the night.

June 5, 1944—Eleventh Field Hospital, Labico, Italy

We worked all night until 11:00 A.M. today. We are being more or less swamped with patients, and they sent for three relief teams, Herb Brinker, Frosty Lowery, and Ed Cantlon. They arrived and took over tonight. The wounded boys say that Rome has definitely fallen, the Third Division entering it last night.

June 6, 1944—Eleventh Field Hospital, Labico, Italy

Today was some day. Gordon Madding, Vince Iovine, and my teams all piled into a truck and went the twenty miles to Rome. We were greeted as conquering heroes, as was every American vehicle. The streets were solidly packed with cheering, clapping, waving, rose-throwing people. All Rome was out on the streets, apparently, and there were more good-looking gals everywhere than we had seen since leaving the States. Rome is practically untouched by war. The people are clean, well dressed, and well nourished. It is the only clean Italian town I have ever seen. Most of the shops were closed, and there was very little in the way of merchandise, apparently. The drinks were good, and the holiday spirit prevailed. Tanks were rolling up the Corso Umberto and the infantry still advancing rapidly north and northwest. We had some pretty good Italian food and wine. We saw the Piazza Venezia and the Mussolini balcony, the Colosseum, the Forum, San Angelo, the Tiber, and Saint Peter's. The latter was thronged with soldiers. In a phone book, Gordon and I looked up Pierre Frugoni's address. Frugoni was an Italian contemporary of ours while we were at the Mayo Clinic. We went out to the address to see if we could locate him. He has a fine apartment home, and we talked with his dad, who seemed delighted to see us and welcomed us profusely. We promised to come back tomorrow.

June 7, 1944—Eleventh Field Hospital, Labico, Italy

Gordon and I each did a case early this morning and slept until noon. We then went into Rome this afternoon and to the Frugoni's apartment. He was there and greeted us, although obviously not re-membering us too well. We started drinking Italian brandy and re-miniscing. Frugoni has had a pretty tough time of it. He has only done four neurosurgical cases in the four years since he returned from Mayo to Italy. He had been assigned to a Corvette in the "Sicilian Channel." He was then sent to France, tried to escape into Spain, was caught by the Gestapo, and escaped again. He has been hiding in a local hospital for the past nine months. A lot of people dropped in, including a gal from Wisconsin formerly named Sorg, who married an Italian diplomat and got caught over here. Gordon, who is from Wisconsin, and she had an old-time reunion. She hadn't heard from her folks for three years. Dinner was quite formal and nice, but not too much food. Wine and champagne were okay. We then sat around talking until about 11:00 P.M., when Pierre took us down to the Excelsior Hotel, where Gordon and I had wonderful rooms with marble baths, clean sheets, et cetera, and so to bed.

June 8, 1944—Eleventh Field Hospital, Labico, Italy
Gordon and I got up, ate breakfast at the Excelsior, and hitchhiked back to camp with a Captain Vora of 2 Corps. Nothing much doing the rest of the day.

June 12, 1944—Eleventh Field Hospital, Labico, Italy
Our tenth wedding aniversary, and entirely different from what I ever expected it to be. I don't like it a bit. We thumbed a truck from the Eleventh Field Hospital and went to Rome to try to find Headquarters, which is reputed to be in Rome. We went around to the military Police headquarters and met a swell guy, Captain Norris, who took us around to the Ninety-fourth, Fifty-sixth, and Fifteenth Evacs, which have moved into Rome. No one knew where our headquarters was. Came back to town and dropped into the Excelsior and had a few martinis.

June 13, 1944—Eleventh Field Hospital, Labico, Italy
Colonel Forsee finally sent us two trucks and a weapons carrier this morning. We had evacuated all our patients. This afternoon we cracked Charlie Westerfield's bottle of cognac and sunbathed, horsed around, and finally did Roman statues, including *Romulus and Remus*. After supper, Colonel Forsee showed up and bulled for a couple of hours. We are to move in the morning at 2:00 A.M.

Chapter III
Rome to the Arno

June 14, 1944—Thirty-third Field Hospital, Orbetello, Italy

We got up at 2:30 A.M., loaded up, and took off. We ditched the convoy, which was going around a back way, and took Highway 6 to Rome and Headquarters. Headquarters is in a swell park just back of the Vatican. Colonel Forsee was just checking out at 6:00 A.M., so we got to see him. We picked up some supplies, ate breakfast, and started out for Civitavechia about 8:30. The ride was nice, through agricultural country, resembling (according to Gordon) the scenery of Wisconsin. German vehicle wrecks were pretty numerous all the way up. Airfields and railyards had been severly bombed everywhere. We arrived at the designated point three miles north of Civitavechia at noon. Civitavechia is a port town that has been heavily bombed and is fairly well flattened. Numerous supply ships of ours were already there, however. "Anzio Annie," the huge railway artillery piece, stood abandoned on back tracks in Civitavecchia. We clambered over it and were properly impressed with its size and length. The Eleventh Field Hospital had already moved on, and no one knew just where. We finally found advanced headquarters of 4 Corps, at Montallo-in-Castio and after a lot of phoning, we found that "Beartracks" Palmer, who is acting 4 Corps Surgeon, the dope, had moved them about ten miles ahead without notifying anyone or anything. We finally located them. We were told that the boys up with the Thirty-third Field Hopsital were in a jam and to go on up to relieve them, so we went on up about four miles northwest of Orbetello and found Jarvis, Hoffman, and Ballentine. Jarvis put on quite a pitiful act about being overworked. We got set up and started working after supper, each team doing two cases and cleaning out the surgical cases. A Jerry I did was horribly shot up in the belly.

June 15, 1944—Thirty-third Field Hospital, Orbetello, Italy

No work today; the artillery around us has moved up, and the boys are pretty close to Grossetto, I understand. This afternoon we went to Orbetello to look around. This town has been pretty well destroyed because of a big seaplane base having been there. Found a bunch of new Italian canteens, and I picked up a couple to send to the boys. We went over to Porto San Stefano, on an island that connects with Orbetello. We were about the only Americans there and were curiosities, the few remaining inhabitants staring at us and following us everywhere. The town had been utterly destroyed by bombs and Jerry demolitions, and there are many sunken ships here. We took a boat ride on an Italian boat across the bay and had a nice time generally. We heard over the BBC tonight that Orbetello had been cut off by the Americans and it was sure to fall. That only happened six days ago. We also saw the remains of an American weapons carrier that had just run down a little lane into a Jerry mine field. Not much left of it. When we got back to the Thirty-third Hospital, we found that Dr. Churchill and other medical dignitaries had visited us and gone over our patients. *Now I regret missing him. He noted this visit in his book* Surgeon to Soldiers *with the following: "We reached a platoon of the 33rd Field Hospital located near Oribello (sic). Tom Ballentine, Luther Wolff, Fred Jarvis, and others of the 2nd Auxiliary Surgical Group made rounds with us, concentrating on a number of seriously wounded men. The triage has been selective and the surgery excellent."*

June 18, 1944—Eleventh Field Hospital, four miles south of Grossetto
A fairly quiet day, although we got four patients in tonight and I stayed up until 3:30 A.M. working. In the afternoon we went up to a battery of Long Toms and had a nice visit with the captain in charge. He asked us what we wanted, and I scared the hell out of him by replying, "We are up for a sanitary and short arm inspection." His face fell and he looked in shock. Finally we took pity on him and explained that we were just looking around. This battery was the same Margaret Bourke-White, the *Life* photographer, photographed last fall back at Presenzano, and the string puller is the same guy. We had him go through the same act for us while we snapped pictures of him for publications in the *Surgery, Gynecology, and Obstetrics Journal.*

June 20, 1944—Eleventh Field Hospital, Grossetto, Italy
We finally got another cigarette ration today. The food here is swell. The mess officer is an MAC officer and is really on the ball, scouting around finding local produce, which helps amazingly. Major Boward, the CO runs a fine platoon.

June 21, 1944—Eleventh Field Hospital, Grossetto, Italy
This afternoon some of us tried to find a spot to take a swim. We went back about twenty miles to a spot across the bay from San Stefano, but found it *no buono*. We decided to explore some of the woods west

104

of Grossetto. All these roads had extensive roadblocks, mine fields and pillboxes, because there is obviously a good invasion point here. The engineers had cleared out the mines. One Jerry truck had been in such a hurry to get out, apparently, that he forgot about the mines and had hit a Teller mine going through a concrete roadblock. The truck landed upside down in a canal, and his cargo was scattered everywhere. The bridges to the coast were blown out, so we never did get a swim. This is a beautiful agricultural section, apparently government-drained land and very fertile and flat. We decided to try to get some eggs and finally wound up with three dozen. These farm people were very suspicious of us at first, but a few cigarettes to the men, candy to the kids, and a volleyball toss to the kids easily won them over.

June 22, 1944—Eleventh Field Hospital

We went on a GI picnic and swim today back to San Stefano—about six nurses, eight officers, and a dozen enlisted men. The water was wonderful, as usual, and the weather fine. I tried a little squid fishing with a couple of Ginsos, but no luck. Thoroughly tired out when we got back. The war is moving rapidly; the Third Platoon has gone about fifteen miles forward.

June 23, 1944—Eleventh Field Hospital

Yesterday we had a couple of Russian POWs brought in. These Russians were asleep in a hayfield when one of our boys found them and tossed a grenade at them. Our enlisted man, Slavik, can talk the lingo and said they were pretty darn sore because they had been so maltreated. They failed to take into account the fact that they had on German uniforms. They were considerably penetrated in numerous places. The Russians have very tough skins, as dulled knives and broken skin needles proved. Colonel Forsee was up hinting about our next little water trip. I did not jump at the chance.

June 24, 1944—Eleventh Field Hospital, Follonica, Italy

We got word at 6:00 P.M. to move up, so we hurriedly got ready and took off. We were given coordinates putting us about three miles north of Follonica. About ten miles short of this point, we started running into large numbers of infantry hiking up the road with combat packs. There were also battalion aid stations and other front line units, so we began to get alarmed. We went on with some trepidation and arrived without getting behind the German lines. We found out that these infantrymen were the Thirty-fourth Division moving up to relieve the Thirty-sixth Division. We finally got set up just before dark.

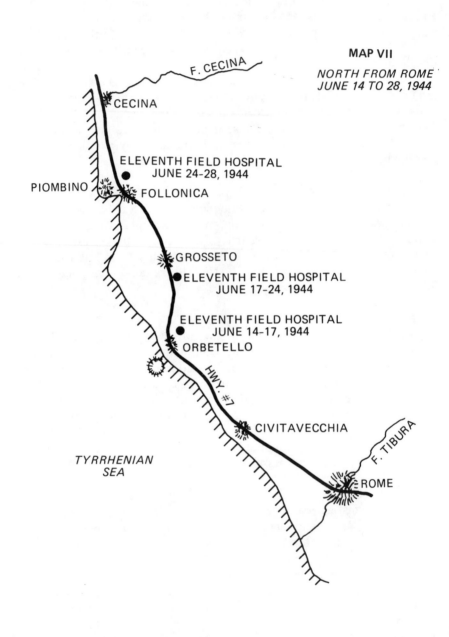

MAP VII

*NORTH FROM ROME
JUNE 14 TO 28, 1944*

F. CECINA

CECINA

ELEVENTH FIELD HOSPITAL
JUNE 24-28, 1944

PIOMBINO

FOLLONICA

GROSSETO

ELEVENTH FIELD HOSPITAL
JUNE 17-24, 1944

ELEVENTH FIELD HOSPITAL
JUNE 14-17, 1944

ORBETELLO

HWY. #7

CIVITAVECCHIA

F. TIBURA

*TYRRHENIAN
SEA*

ROME

June 25, 1944—Eleventh Field Hospital, Follonica, Italy

This afternoon Gordon and I were off, so we went into Follonica and did a bit of looking around. There is a wonderful beach running clear back to Piombino. We were a little leery of mines and the extensive barbed-wire defenses were very evident, so we didn't explore it too much. After we got back to the hospital, BBC announced that the Americans had taken Follonica. Tonight we had a number of cases. Gordon and I weren't on call, since Tom Ballentine had come up to make the fourth team, but we went ahead on two kids, both of whom had both legs blown off by a shell that landed in their foxhole, which they were occupying together.

June 27, 1944—Eleventh Field Hospital, near Follonica, Italy

This afternoon Howard Snyder visited us, and we went up eleven miles to Unit II of the Eleventh Field Hospital. Poor Henry Hoffman and Blocksom had been having a rough time of it, the usual mixup of not having four teams in the most forward unit. We went on around to Piombino. This town is an industrial town with a very large steel mill. The air boys really did a job on it, utterly demolishing it. Bombs seems to be most effective for a job like this. One sees huge craters around bridges frequently, where they tried to knock out the bridge, with utter lack of success.

June 28, 1944—683d Clearing Company, Gabellino, Italy

We got our moving orders just before noon, to proceed inland through Massa Marettina, Prata, and up to a crossroads called Gabellino, where the Fifty-fourth Medics Clearing Station was located, backing up the First Armored, and one combat team of the Ninety-first Division, which is a newly arrived division. Gordon and I won (?) the privilege of going. It was raining when we started off. My confrers ribbed me unmercifully about my insistance on maps, coordinates, and orientation, but I always have gotten them to any given spot without getting lost, and it is much easier on the nerves to know exactly where one is in relation to the front. The country is very hilly and wooded, and the roads are all gravel, which the rain improves considerably as far as dust is concerned. Our artillery caught a German horse-drawn outfit going up a hill beyond Massa, and the bloated, stinking horse bodies were all along the road, with quantities of wrecked carts and so forth. The Fifty-fourth Medics are set up in a nice spot on rising ground. Soon after we got set up, the battery of Long Toms adjacent to the hospital pulled out. This is a relief. The 683d Clearing Station was poorly set up for us to work in, since they were a new outfit, but they welcomed us nicely and couldn't do too much for us. They had no blood, no IV fluids, no rubber tubing, et cetera, but they sent a messenger and got all these things before we got any patients in. I did one nice belly case this evening, having a very extensive gallery of clearing station officers in the tent and enlisted men peeping in under all the rolled-up tent flaps. We did some hamming during the surgery to impress them.

June 29, 1944—683d Clearing Station, Gabellino, Italy

This outfit is on the ball. Their CO, Captain Finnen, is an older man, who runs a good mess and a well-disciplined outfit. A good many casualties are coming in, but very few serious ones. Ben Burbanks, our shock man, likes to treat these chest cases conservatively, which we let him do with our grateful thanks. The Thirty-third Field Hospital (Shatic's platoon) pulled in tonight and got set up remarkably quickly near us. We have arranged to keep on eating with the clearing station; the Thirty-third just don't know how to run a mess, and the sad part is they think they are a real hot outfit. Charlie and I did some scavenging in the countryside for produce this afternoon. On our foraging trip, we ran into a couple of Italian youths who had a young hawk, constrained by a leg string, but quite tame! We all miss pets very much, and after a good deal of dickering with the Italians, we acquired the hawk for a few packages of cigarettes. In discussing a name for him, Paul Kennedy hit upon the name "Lutrochar," which has a nice medieval ring and is derived from the first syllable of our team's first names, viz, Luther, Troglar, and Charles equals Lutrochar. Had a belly case this A.M., a forty-nine-year–old fat Italian shot by Jerries for being a partisan. His guts were rotten when I got him, and he is sure to die.

June 30, 1944—Thirty-third Field Hospital, Gabellino, Italy

This is the way I like to work, about one good case a day. We had a boy from North Carolina today with extensive wounds of the rectum, bladder, ileum, jejunum, and so forth. Trogh undertook him, but tired out and I finished him. The days pass rapidly somehow. I got a couple of letters from M. W., which I needed very badly indeed.

July 1, 1944—Thirty-third Field Hospital, Gabellino, Italy

This morning the Thirty-third Field Hospital moved up about twenty miles and left my team behind as a holding unit to look after our five cases. I went up with the other teams, to bring back the weapons carrier, which I did. The road was one cloud of dust, and everyone

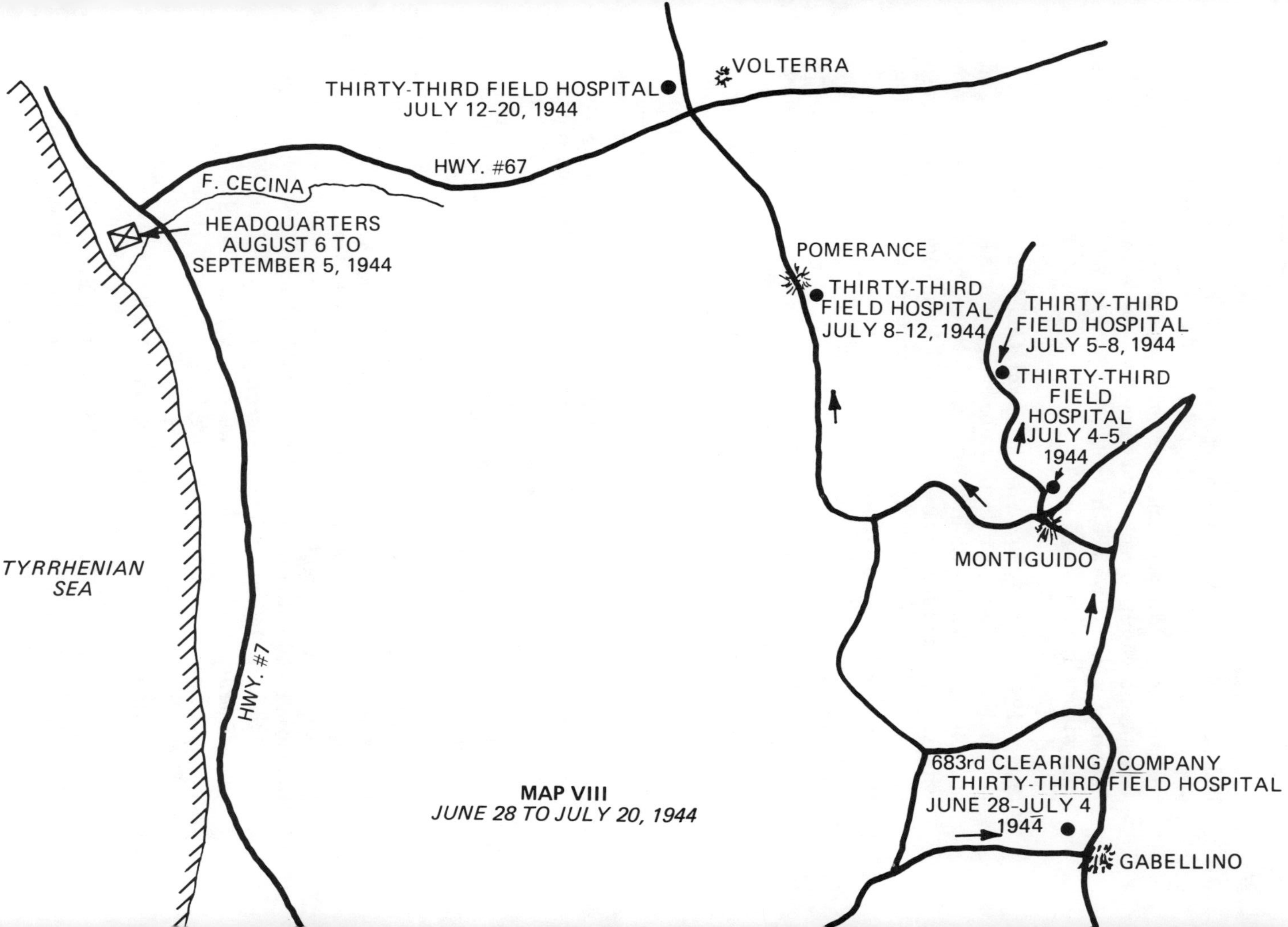

THIRTY-THIRD FIELD HOSPITAL
JULY 12-20, 1944

VOLTERRA

HWY. #67

F. CECINA

HEADQUARTERS
AUGUST 6 TO
SEPTEMBER 5, 1944

POMERANCE

THIRTY-THIRD
FIELD HOSPITAL
JULY 8-12, 1944

THIRTY-THIRD
FIELD HOSPITAL
JULY 5-8, 1944

THIRTY-THIRD
FIELD
HOSPITAL
JULY 4-5,
1944

MONTIGUIDO

683rd CLEARING COMPANY
THIRTY-THIRD FIELD HOSPITAL
JUNE 28-JULY 4
1944

GABELLINO

HWY. #7

TYRRHENIAN
SEA

MAP VIII
JUNE 28 TO JULY 20, 1944

looked like grotesque caricatures of themselves. This afternoon, Charlie and I went about the countryside, foraging for lettuce *(ensilata)*, chickens, and eggs, with some success. We only have fifteen people in this attachment, with two cooks and three KPs, so we intend to live high! Beautiful weather we are having, with nice moonlight nights. This valley is really beautiful.

July 2, 1944—Thirty-third Field Hospital, Gabellino, Italy
Nothing to do except sleep, sunbathe, catch the hawk lizards, and eat. Oh, how we are eating! Fresh eggs, lettuce and onion salad, with wine vinegar, and tonight fresh peach pie! A fine life! Our hawk is so tame that we have removed all the restraints except a clipped wing. He seems quite satisfied living with us as long as we bring him enough lizards.

July 4, 1944—Thirty-third Field Hospital, ten miles north of Montieri, Italy, on the Cecina River
We evacuated our patients this morning, packed up, and joined the others at this location this afternoon. The tents are pitched right on the banks of this little river that resembles a trout stream back home. We took a bath in the river and got some of the dust off us and pretty nearly froze. Tonight we had a steak roast. One of our nurses, Miss Herrell, had bought twenty-five pounds of local beef. They found maggots in it and it was tough as shoe leather, but we were not told about these unappetizing details until after we had all eaten some.

July 5, 1944—Thirty-third Field Hospital, near Montiguido, Italy
We pulled up here today, strictly cross-country. The engineers had constructed this "road" straight across the country, which is very mountainous. There was no road here formerly. The dust is six inches deep. If it ever rained, everything would be completely stalled. The First Armored Division is working through here; no one can determine why. It is strictly not a tank country. Frank Hall, Sorehead Poole, Tom Ballentine, and I and our teams are here. Gordon and Fred Jarvis were pulled back to Headquarters this morning to acquire Duck Feet. Fourteen general surgical teams and twenty-four teams in all are going on the next little trip (southern France).

July 6, 1944—Thirty-third Field Hospital, Montiguido
This morning, we borrowed Tom Ballentine's jeep, Frank Hall's team got in their jeep, and we all took off for Siena. We went over through the French sector, nobody being able to tell us whether we

would get through or not, but we did without incident. Siena is a very quaint city, strictly medieval, and hasn't changed much in centuries. It is entirely undamaged by the war. The cathedral is quite a structure, resembling a zebra with its alternate layers of black and white marble. We visited the medical schools where Tony Emmi had taken his training, but it was closed. We also went to the principal hospitals across from the cathedral. Their medicine and surgery in my opinion is quite medieval also, from what I can see. All their faith is put in various local concoctions. They have no intravenous fluids, no Wangensteen suctions, no nothing. Skin-tight plasters with the bone fragments in poor position are applied. We had an ugly incident with some British officers at lunch. Remind me to dislike the British. The trip back was as dusty as the one going.

July 7, 1944—Thirty-third Field Hospital, Pomerance, Italy
We got up early, packed up, and moved straight west for about twenty miles to cover about eight northerly airline miles. We are now backing up the Eighty-eighth Division, which went in yesterday. By noon, the casualties started rolling in, and although we went off duty at 4:00 P.M., we did two cases after that. Looks like a tough seige ahead. Our hawk is fitting into our lives nicely. We catch a lizard or two every day, which he seems to enjoy thoroughly.

July 9, 1944—Thirty-third Field Hospital, Pomerance, Italy
We worked steadily from 8:00 A.M. to 10:00 P.M. doing four bellies and a chest. I certainly have had some easy bellies lately, however. The casualties are still pouring in. I surely miss Gordon and his team in a push period like this! There is so much dawdling by some of the other teams!

July 10, 1944—Thirty-third Field Hospital, Pomerance, Italy
We got up early and checked out for Headquarters, going to Cecina, a trip of seventy-miles or so, fearfully dusty. Headquarters is near the mouth of the Cecina River, between Follonica and Piombino, and is set up in an olive grove. Practically everyone is back at Headquarters; I never saw so many teams together. They have a bar, a recreation tent, and everything. The other teams all seemed glad to see me. I had a little talk with Colonel Forsee and told him I wouldn't object if he sent me on the next trip. Besides, I am getting awfully fed up with the Thirty-third Field Hospital and am afraid I'll be stuck here in Italy with it. So many of the boys are going to France that I feel like a slacker, almost.

July 11, 1944—Thirty-third Field Headquarters, Pomerance, Italy

We got back from Headquarters, and I went to work at 4:00 P.M., working straight through until 8:00 the next morning, doing four bellies and a chest. Gosh, am I tired! There is talk of moving again.

July 12, 1944—Thirty-third Field Hospital, four miles west of Volterra, Italy

We operated all day yesterday, and after supper word came through to move. We are still with the First Platoon, and I am saddled with the job of being senior surgeon again. Larry Shefts, Henry Hoffman, and Tom Ballentine are the other teams of this unit. I had to leave Tom Ballentine back as a holding platoon. The ten miles or so to our new location were very dusty. We got set up just about dark.

July 13, 1944—Thirty-third Field Hospital, Volterra, Italy

This is a fine business! We did two cases this morning, and just at noon a message came through for Charlie to get back to Headquarters at once. So he got packed up and took off. I sure hate to see him leave; he is a swell guy, besides being a wonderful anesthesiologist. They sent me Miss Barrett as a replacement. We did three more cases after she arrived; she is okay, but not nearly as good as Charlie. I guess we will make out okay, though. I caught the bird a couple of snakes today, curious little brown fellows with three yellow vertical stripes, and as fast as a greased pig. The bird swallows them practically whole. Incidentally, these snakes have very appreciable rudimentary legs and may be nothing more than a peculiar type of lizard.

July 14, 1944—Volterra, Italy

Things eased up a bit today. Maj. George Stephenson, a Mayo man who was my senior there, had been in the Aleutians but had no work there. He joined us up here to get broken in. I went back to Pomerance and got Tom Ballentine and his team, except for Shepard, his assistant surgeon. Steve works with Tom, so we have four teams now. This afternoon when Steve came in, there were seven guys with legs blown off by Shue mines in surgery and in the shock tent; and Henry and I were reamputating at a great rate. These mines are vicious up ahead, they say.

July 15, 1944—Thirty-third Field Hospital, Volterra, Italy

We went up to Volterra this afternoon. It is a very quaint medieval town perched on the summit of a very high hill or low mountain. The view is beautiful from up there. There are a lot of very old buildings and castles. I left my laundry to be done there.

112

July 1944 near Volterra, Italy—our pet hawk, Lutrochar, tackles a lizard and gets his upper bill bit.

My team (G.S. No 15), summer 1944, Tuscany. Left to right. Kneeling: Dunlop, Donald Scott ("Scotty"). Back row: Lt. Frances Mosher, L.H.W., Trog Adkins, assistant and Bess Barett, anesthetist.

July 16, 1944—Thirty-third Field Hospital, Volterra, Italy

Went back up to Volterra this morning. We barged through the Palazzo dei Pieori clear up to the call tower. There are some nice, very old paintings throughout this old castle, with a tremendous number of coats of arms. It seems that Volterra is the alabaster center of Italy, and by today a lot of stuff had blossomed out. Some of the things looked pretty nice and are quite reasonably priced. I got a bunch of stuff for the kids and for Mary Will, and I hope they will like these articles. I got my laundry this afternoon and bought a lot of lettuce, onions, and cucumbers and some garlic. I had the nurses fix up a salad, which we ate tonight and enjoyed thoroughly. This green stuff was the first we had had in a couple of weeks. I jumped all over this Thirty-third Field Hospital outfit because of their mess today, since a shortage of canned corn gave me the opportunity. They've been asking for a chewing out for a long time.

July 19, 1944—Thirty-third Field Hospital, three miles east of Peccioli, Italy

We moved up here this morning and set up but had little or nothing to do. The Eighty-eighth Division has taken all the ground south of the Arno River in this sector, and we will wait here until the others catch up. Tonight we heard that Livorno has been taken.

July 21, 1944—Thirty-third Field Hospital, Peccioli, Italy

Nothing much going on. A surgical team from the Forty-fifth General Hospital joined us, headed by Captain Massey, a nice fellow. We played volleyball with the Eighty-eighth Clearing Station boys every evening, and tonight I sprained my right patella tendon severely. I just ain't as young as I once was.

July 23, 1944—Peccioli, Italy

Captain Massey's team was sent over to the Thirty-eighth Evac, and another base team, Major Ilgenfritz's team, from the Sixty-fourth General Hospital, joined us. He is assistant professor of surgery at LSU and has written quite a bit. He is very anxious to do an acute belly case, something that he has not done in a long time.

July 26, 1944—Peccioli, Italy

Went back to Headquarters near Cecina today with Trogh, who is hitting the old man for a team of his own, so he can get a promotion. Colonel Forsee talked encouragingly enough. Gene Caldwell was there, and we had a little Yocky-Docky and talked various things and people over. After lunch, we drove up to Leghorn. This city is situated on the coast, on flat ground, below the mouth of the Arno. It is rather beautiful as seen from the top of a mountain we were forced to cross because all the bridges had been blown so we didn't get to see it closely, no matter how fast we talked to the MPs.

August 1, 1944—Thirty-third Field Hospital, Peccioli, Italy
Joe Lalich, who is a good shock man, and I went on a little foraging expedition yesterday, looking for a cow. We went on a back road south and east of here. Picked up a nice-looking boy who had been on the Russian front for a year or so. He took us around to various farmhouses, and we acquired vinegar, onions, and garlic. Nothing much going on today. I got some fine letters and pictures of the kids from Mary Will. This being away from home at this stage of the kids' development is a great loss to me and probably to them.

August 3, 1944—Thirty-third Field Hospital, Peccioli
Miss Barrett and Miss Muhs, two of our nurses, got their promotions to first lieutenant, so we threw a party for them tonight. There is a distinct lack of cordiality between our nurses, the attached Sixty-fourth General Hospital nurse, and the Thirty-third Field Hospital nurses. The party wasn't too much of a success. Our stag parties always are much more fun, for some reason.

August 4, 1944—Thirty-third Field Hospital, Peccioli
Stephenson wanted to go back to Headquarters to see the colonel, so Trogh, Henry Hoffman, and I decided to go along. The damn weapons carrier would run along for a mile or so, then die down and cease. Some sort of vapor lock, apparently. We finally got there, only to find that the colonel was up seeing us at the Thirty-third Field. So we went back to the Thirty-third Field, only to just miss him again. He talked to some of the guys around here about getting some of the teams back to Headquarters for rest.

August 5, 1944—Thirty-third Field Hospital, Peccioli
I got a note today from Colonel Forsee ordering my team back to Headquarters, presumably for a "rest." We haven't done anything for a couple of weeks, but a change won't be so bad, I guess. We released our pet hawk, who had started to fly again. So, we think he will be all right on his own. We were afraid that we would be unable to catch enough lizards and snakes back at Headquarters to feed him there.

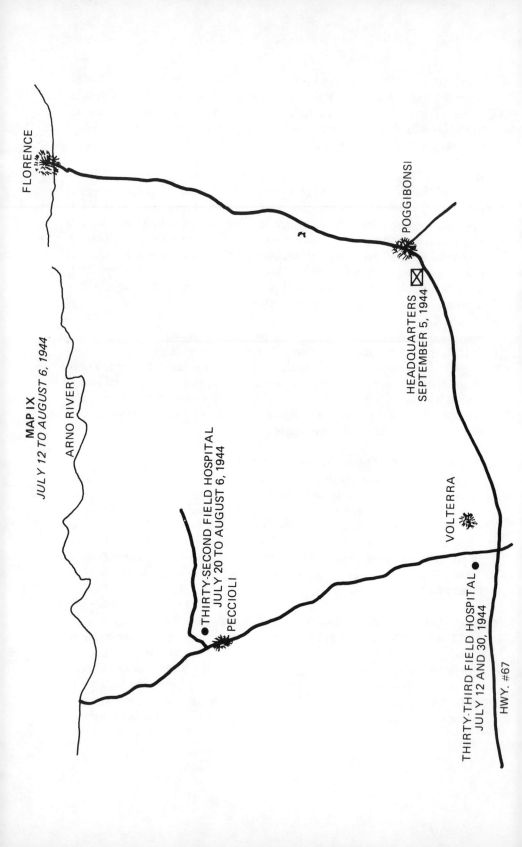

MAP IX
JULY 12 TO AUGUST 6, 1944

FLORENCE

ARNO RIVER

POGGIBONSI

HEADQUARTERS
SEPTEMBER 5, 1944

●THIRTY-SECOND FIELD HOSPITAL
JULY 20 TO AUGUST 6, 1944

PECCIOLI ●

VOLTERRA

THIRTY-THIRD FIELD HOSPITAL ●
JULY 12 AND 30, 1944

HWY. #67

August 6, 1944—Headquarters, Cecina

We got packed up this morning and came on back to Headquarters this afternoon. There are quite a few teams back here: Hopkins, Red Robby, Sorehead Poole, Jim Mason, Larry Hunt, and others. It's nice to see all these fellows again. Headquarters is beautifully situated and is very nicely fixed up, with showers, volleyball courts, horseshoes, et cetera. The de-mined beach is only a couple of hundred yards away. Instead of being parked in a stubble field, we are, for a change, bivouacked in a beautiful grove of pine trees, trimmed in the usual Italian manner so that they look like umbrellas. Black Robbie threw a mild Yocky-Docky party tonight, and we sat around batting the breeze in the moonlight. Somewhat nostalgic, though.

August 7, 1944—Cecina, Italy

Everyone has been afraid to go near the beach around here, since a colonel from an artillery outfit took a shortcut coming back from the beach and stepped on a box mine. The remains were hard to find. Taylor and I went down to scout out the situation and decided it was perfectly safe, since there are cleared areas clearly marked. So we had a nice swim.

August 9, 1944—Headquarters, Cecina

Today was much like the other days. Major Rivenbark, who is with the Sixty-fourth General Hospital, dropped in today and I had a nice talk with him. He is the brother of my brother Carl's partner, and a pediatrician. He seems like a nice fellow, but very young-looking for his age. From what I can gather from his conversation, this general hospital life must be quite horrible.

August 11, 1944—Excelsior Hotel, Rome

George Hopkins, Red Robby, Trogh, and I loaded up in a weapons carrier this morning and took off at 9:00 for Rome and a "rest." I had to drive the 190 miles down here, and it was a long, hard trip. Many caustic comments from the back from Trogh and Hoppy whenever I hit a bump. Trogh and I are rooming together in Room 453—twin beds, inner spring mattresses, swell marble bath, and wonderful service and food. This fellow Kline who is running the Excelsior Hotel is doing a fine job, but he is really fighting a hard war. He has acquired a lieutenant colonelcy, an expert infantryman's badge, and wears a dust scarf at all times to protect against these fierce clouds of dust that are raised in the lobby of the hotel. It is all very touching. The Italian gals flock in by the scores. All males have to show their ID cards to the MPs to even get through the first gate, but females wander in and out at will without any checking. It is said that some of these girls came in with the first officers two months ago and have never left the hotel since.

August 12, 1944—Excelsior, Rome

The food here is simply wonderful; everything is cooked by the Italian staff, and they surely know how to cook. This afternoon Robbie, Trogh, and I went out to see Pierre Frugoni and persuaded him, his girlfriend, the former Rosetta Sorge, and her husband to come to dinner with us. We took them up before dinner and introduced them to the fine old army drink Yocky-Docky. After dinner, which they enjoyed immensely, we went back out to Pierre's house, where we sat on the terrace drinking, talking, and listening to the phonograph. A very pleasant evening.

August 13, 1944—Excelsior Hotel, Rome

Today we picked up Frugoni and his Italian friends and took them swimming. They hadn't been out of Rome for months, but decided that the best beaches were at Anzio, so back to Anzio we went, a place I thought I would never see again. There is absolutely nothing there anymore except for some salvage crews. The hospital area is just a bunch of holes and mounds of dirt. The air strip is all grown over with weeds through the steel matting. We went out to Red Beach, the Third Division landing beach, and had a wonderful swim and picnic lunch. There is still considerable debris of war scattered about. We went down by way of "the Factory" and came back by way of Cisterna and Valletria. These Italian friends oohed and aahed all over the place when they saw the destruction of these places. I'm sure they never realized what war was like before. We got back just in time to get supper at 9:00 P.M., had a good bottle of wine and a good meal. Went to bed all tired out.

August 15, 1944—Headquarters, Cecina

We drove back from Rome yesterday, a tiresome 200-mile trip. The news of the invasion of southern France came through at 1:00 P.M. on the 1:00 P.M. broadcast. We listened with a lot of interest and a little envy. I sure don't want to get stuck here for the rest of the war in Italy! Howard Snyder was around and we had quite a discussion about tourniquets. He wants me to write a paper on the use of tourniquets. *This handling of tourniquets by the army medical service has been bothering me ever since I saw a fine young infantry captain bleed to death a month or so ago from a small shell fragment that had partially severed his left*

*brachial artery. This was the only wound he had anywhere. While he
was being transported from the front (a matter of six or seven hours)
the tourniquet that had been applied above the wound was carefully
released every twenty minutes in compliance with the standard army
directive regarding the handling of tourniquets. He arrived back at the
clearing station almost completely exsanguinated and in extremis, lying
in a gallon or more of blood on his stretcher. He was rushed over to our
field hospital, where he shortly thereafter died, despite hurried infusions
of plasma. This antiquated and atrocious handling of tourniquets, as
directed in the army directives, certainly needs revising, and if a paper
will do any good, I will be happy to write it.*

August 17, 1944—Headquarters, Cecina
I have developed a horrible cold, which I attribute to the Rome
visit. New human contacts, beds, rooms, et cetera. Apparently I don't
tolerate civilization anymore. Things are really moving along encouragingly in France.

August 18, 1944—Headquarters, Cecina
We have a nice bar set up in our recreation tent, and the nurses
fix swell sandwiches every night, so that we eat plenty, almost four
meals a day. It is becoming quite a joke around here, and I am forced
to accept plenty of razzing from the guys because of the way I demand
tomatoes four times a day. These tomatoes sure help out.

August 19, 1944—Headquarters, Cecina
I saw Colonel Forsee today regarding the paper on tourniquets.
He seemed quite enthusiastic and is ready for me to get started on it.
So I did. No one suffers from composition as much as I do. It is pure
agony, and why I ever undertake such work I will never understand.

August 20, 1944—Headquarters, Cecina
Worked on my paper practically all day, but welcomed any distrac-
tion, such as newscasts, horseshoes, volleyball, and what have you, as
an excuse to stop working.

August 23, 1944—Headquarters, Cecina
Colonel Howard Beecher visited us and went over the rough draft
of my paper and seemed to think I had something good going. He made
a few suggestions. I finished it up today, but it needs considerable
reorganization.

August 24, 1944—Headquarters, Cecina

Colonel Forsee wanted to see my paper, so I let him wade through it in its original form. He complimented me on it and said it "was of fundamental importance." Trogh talked about putting in for a Legion of Merit for me with Colonel Forsee.

August 30, 1944—Headquarters, Cecina

We have had a nice time this afternoon. We had gotten to know the officers of the heavy pontoon engineering outfit near us, and they invited us to go out in the boat with them. We said, "Okay," so Tony Emmi, Glen, Joe Lalich, Hoppy Hopkins, Taylor, and I went on this trip. We made quite a procession, representing a vast investment. First there was a truck towing the trailer that carried a boat (about a fifteen-foot boat with a large marine inboard motor). Then there was a weapons carrier (ours), then a command car, then a huge crane to lift the boat in and out of the water. We went up the coast about six miles to a pier that the Germans had partially wrecked. Boats were sunk everywhere. The beaches were heavily mined, and warning signs were everywhere. The crane put the boat in the water, and a Captain Armstrong, Joe Lalich, a lieutenant, and I went out. The rest were afraid of "floating mines" and backed down. The aquaplaning of this powerful boat was wonderful; the Tyrrhenian Sea was calm, blue, and utterly delightful. The other guys decided it was okay when we didn't get blown up, so we went back in for them. Some Eyeties were trying to salvage some ship motors in a sunken boat. They asked if the crane would help them instead of the laborious chain hoist method they were using. In about ten minutes, all the motors were lifted and ashore, a two weeks job for them.

September 2, 1944

It rained hard last night for a short time. We went swimming this afternoon, there being a strong wind from the west for the last couple of days, and the water was wonderfully rough. We took mattress covers and rode the waves like we were on surfboards. A good many people talked a lot about undertow, but personally I don't see anything to become alarmed about.

September 5, 1944—Headquarters, Poggibonsi

This morning, the whole headquarters personnel moved up to two miles west of Poggibonsi. We are set up in an orchard and vineyard, quite a nice place. The hills are on all sides of us, and San Giuimagno is about 4 miles west of us, perched on top of a mountain. San Giuimagno has a high wall around it, and it is noted for its medieval skyscrapers. For some inexplicable reason, the palaces in town jut up five or six stories high and serve no useful purpose except to provide leg exercises for the inhabitants, as far as I can see.

September 8, 1944—Headquarters, Poggibonsi

It cleared up today after three days of constant rain. Red Robby had arranged a trip to Florence for us. Getting to Florence involved a lot of traffic jams because there is only one Bailey bridge across the Arno River just to the west of Florence. The Germans had demolished every other bridge except the Ponte Vecchio, which they had effectively blocked by blowing down all the buildings at either end of the bridge. Florence isn't nearly all it is cracked up to be, as far as I can see. It isn't nearly as nice as Rome; the people, particularly the gals, aren't nearly so attractive, and the shops have nothing but junk in them at outrageous prices. I didn't buy a thing or see anything I wanted to buy. We had dinner at the Excelsior Hotel Allied Officers Club, which was very good indeed, with wine being excellent. D-Day Taylor and I got quite a glow out of it. We roamed about downtown Florence all afternoon but found nothing of particular interest.

September 9, 1944—Headquarters, Poggibonsi

Today was a quiet day, and I worked sporadically on my reports. This evening, Taylor, Giddings, and I walked up to the top of the hill nearby and visited a while with an Italian family, using gestures and pig Latin. There were the usual twenty-five people living in the one house, with two women hanging out of a window with swollen jaws from toothaches. There just isn't any dentistry in this country that I can detect. These people stare at us with awe. I don't think they can begin to make us out at all.

September 11, 1944—Headquarters, Poggibonsi

Taylor, Phil Giddings, John Nottinger, and I wheedled a command car from Black Robby for the day, with the original idea of going over to the Adriatic side of the Italian peninsula. We gave it up on looking at the map long enough and decided to go to Pisa instead. So, with our man Scotty to drive us, we took off after breakfast, carrying our lunch. We stopped in San Giuimagno and bought a couple of bottles of wine. The drive to Pisa on Highway 67 is a beautiful drive, and this is an excellent road, the first concrete road I have seen since leaving the States. All the towns in the Arno Valley are frightfully shattered from bombings. There was no bridge across the Arno except a pontoon bridge

121

about five miles below Pisa. South Pisa is the scene of utter ruin and desolation, a veritable ghost city. We lunched along the road. I went to a nearby farmhouse and acquired a goodly supply of tomatoes. Pisa is "off limits," but we talked the MP into letting us in. Immediately on entering the gate of the city wall, the main features of Pisa hit you: the baptistry, the cathedral, the bell tower, better known as the Leaning Tower. The three buildings are architecturally the same as far as I could tell and are really quite beautiful. The tower actually does lean, and one can readily see how they tried to straighten it as they built it, it being curved. It is about 130 or 140 feet high. We walked up in it, taking pictures here and there. Fortunately, none of these three buildings was injured much by the war. The cathedral is the usual black and white marble on the inside and has nice paintings. I was particularly intrigued by the echoes of the baptistry. The doorman would sing the notes of a scale, and the echoes would come back, sounding like a harmonious choir singing. Why anyone would want such an elaborate structure for a baptism, I don't know.

Chapter IV
North Apennines

September 13, 1944—Thirty-third Field Hospital, Second Platoon, near Vaglia, Italy

It is widely known that we are about to start a drive on the Gothic Line north of Florence. The Gothic Line is the main ridge of the Apennines. About 10:00 this morning, we got orders to pack up and leave after lunch, which we did. D-Day Taylor and I came up to the Second Platoon of the Thirty-third Field Hospital, which is operating near Vaglia. This town is about twelve miles north of Florence on Highway 65, which is the main highway between Florence and Bologna. Reeve Betts, Sorehead Poole, and Red Robbie are in this platoon and had been very busy. We are relieving them of some of their duties.

September 14, 1944—First Platoon, Thirty-second Field Hospital, two miles north of San Piero a Sieve and we all are stuck out like sore thumbs.

We did one case this morning, then got orders to move up six miles to the town mentioned above. There is a constant smoke screen over the bridge that spans the Sieve, which we blithely drove through. Smoke screens mean direct enemy observation, and we are sitting right in sight of the Germans. The main ridge of the Apennines and the Gothic Line start about four miles before us, the Artillery is before us, behind us, and to the sides—155 Howitzers, Long Toms, 203s, and behind us 8-inch rifles and 240 mm. Howitzers. We stand and watch the shells land all over the sides of the mountains, day and night. It is really noisy here, reminds me a good deal of Mount Maggiore back last November and December. The Thirty-second Field Hospital seems like a swell outfit, very congenial and obliging. Major Voges is the CO of this platoon. Alex Little of Valdosta, Georgia, who was just starting his fellowship at Mayo about the time I finished, is with this platoon, but not doing much surgery. He is wild to get into the Second Aux., but was turned down by Natousa. So far no Jerry shells have hit near

123

us, but we have heard plenty of them crumping a mile or so away. I have got a nice ditch all lined up for a quick dive. Did one case tonight.

September 15, 1944—Thirty-second Field Hospital, near San Piero

This is surely a hot spot. The artillery is simply everywhere. Today most of our shells were hitting about halfway up the mountain. Casualties are fairly heavy, but not too much so, considering what the boys are up against. They are even making a good advance up the mountain. We are evacuating from the Eighty-fifth Division; the British are on our right and the Ninety-first Division on our left. The Thirty-fourth is next in line on the left on either side of the highway (Highway 65), pushing up toward the Futa Pass. The Eighty-fifth is gaining the most ground and is well inside the first Gothic Line defenses. We have been rather busy. I had to take out ten or fifteen feet of a guy's small intestine today, leaving only about six feet.

September 16, 1944—Thirty-second Field Hospital, San Piero

This morning, Glen Gummess and I walked up the road about a mile to an Italian civilian hospital that was set up in a monastery. The place is run by two Eyetie doctors. They had about sixty patients, mostly old people with degenerative diseases. The sanitation situation was very gruesome despite the fact that dozens of relatives were standing around doing nothing. I am convinced Italy is still essentially a medieval country. There were two cases of minor shrapnel wounds in the hospital, both of which just had a dressing applied and were dreadfully infected, brawny cellulitis and the patients very toxic. We came back by a division POW cage and looked at the haul. There were about fifty dirty, long-haired Jerries, all seeming to be very happy about being out of it. They were lolling about a haystack and could have escaped easily, but obviously didn't want to. There was one guy who spoke good English and was a former member of the New York Bund. He was a nasty individual in looks and the way he acted. Tonight, just at suppertime, German 170s started whining overhead, hitting the Division CP about 500 yards behind us. Most of the Second Aux. guys dived into the ditch and stayed there. The Thirty-second personnel didn't show much concern, but they will learn. The shells came over at intervals for about an hour. We got two soliders and two civilian casualties in here from the shelling. It is silly putting these hospitals this far up. We worked all night and expected to have shells hitting all night, but none did.

124

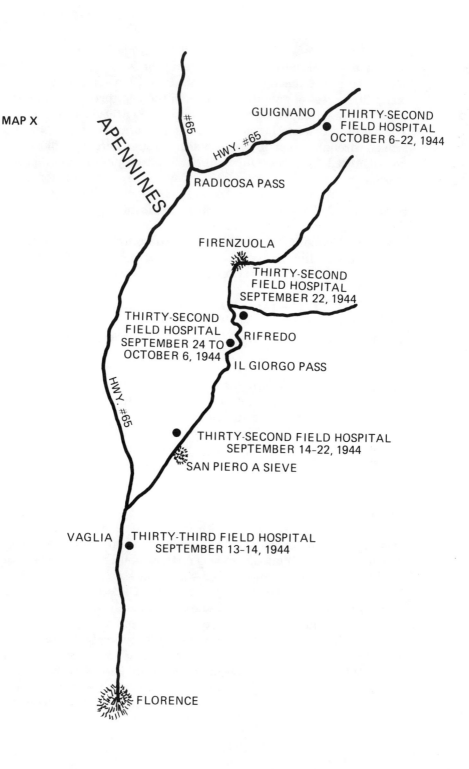

MAP X

APENNINES

#65

HWY. #65

GUIGNANO

THIRTY-SECOND
FIELD HOSPITAL
OCTOBER 6–22, 1944

RADICOSA PASS

FIRENZUOLA

THIRTY-SECOND
FIELD HOSPITAL
SEPTEMBER 22, 1944

THIRTY-SECOND
FIELD HOSPITAL
SEPTEMBER 24 TO
OCTOBER 6, 1944

RIFREDO

IL GIORGO PASS

HWY. #65

THIRTY-SECOND FIELD HOSPITAL
SEPTEMBER 14–22, 1944

SAN PIERO A SIEVE

VAGLIA

THIRTY-THIRD FIELD HOSPITAL
SEPTEMBER 13–14, 1944

FLORENCE

September 17, 1944—Thirty-second Field Hospital, San Piero

We are working hard, but we really haven't been overwhelmed. There is a rather steady flow of admissions. I have never taken out so many linear feet of guts in my life as in the last three days; had three cases that required resection of from six to fifteen feet of small intestine. The shelling is over the pass, over the mountain, and the boys have broken through. No more Jerry shelling around here. Our flanks have not advanced, however. Our mail has been very poor lately for some reason.

September 19, 1944—Thirty-second Field Hospital, San Piero

The four auxiliary surgical teams working here are Hopkins, Hurt, Taylor, and Trogh and I. Captain Peaven, from the Sixteenth Evac, is our shock man, living in our tent. He was formerly with the 602 Clearing Station with us at Paestum.

September 20, 1944—Thirty-second Field Hospital, San Piero

Things are pretty quiet. We got our first liquor ration, real U.S. bourbon, today and is it good! I drew a bottle of Seagrams V.O., which is the best.

September 21, 1944—Thirty-second Field Hospital, San Piero

Not much doing today. According to the BBC, the war is practically over, but the boys trying to get through these mountains think differently, and so do we. The Thirty-fourth and the Ninety-first have gained practically nothing; nor have the British on our right. However, here we can easily see traffic going over the mountain through the Giorgo Pass in our sector.

September 23, 1944—Thirty-sixth Evac Hospital, near Scarperia, Italy

I guess the good Lord is with us, all right. We missed death by inches. Yesterday morning, Black Robby came up and told us to move up with the Third Platoon of the Thirty-second Field Hospital. Larry Hurt drew the lucky number and stayed back as holding. I talked to Major Duncan, of the Eighty-fifth Division Clearing Station, and he said it was mighty hot up there. The executive officer of the Thirty-second Field Hospital, which is a green outfit, and a Major Young came by. I told those guys of the Thirty-second that they had better be sure what they were doing. They looked at me as if I were crazy. Anyhow, we loaded up and took off over the mountain. It took over an hour to go the five miles up the mountain. Traffic bumper to bumper all the way, the barbed wire entanglements, pillboxes, and other fortifications

Over the crest of the Apennines at Il Giorgo Pass, Highway 6524, September 23, 1944.

September 23, 1944—remains of jeep hit twenty-five yards from our hospital by a 170 mm shell while we were setting up at cross-roads two hours after crossing mountains through Giorgo Pass.

were quite noticeable if one looked closely. The upper one-third of the mountain was covered with pine trees about eight inches in diameter. Our artillery had made kindling wood out of it, as well as destroying three wooden barracks the Germans had had near the top. I still don't see how our Eighty-fifth Division guys ever took this mountain. We went to our new location, a hamlet called Castel Nuova, about two and a half miles south of Firenzuola. We immediately saw the situation was bad. We were on a small ridge right next to a crossroads and right next to a battery of 105 Howitzers, which are division light artillery. We ate supper and pitched our tents, and I started digging a foxhole in the tent, planning to sleep in it. I had gone down about six inches when a shell crashed about 200 yards away. All the Second Aux. people hit the ground. The Thirty-second Field Hospital people thought we had gone nuts, they never having heard a shell hit before. A few minutes later, a loud whine came over just to the west of us with crashing explosion. I resumed my digging with fervor. A few minutes later, there was a tremendous concussion wave. Dirt, rocks, and debris showered around us; a tire and wheel came sailing through the air and hit about five feet from me. Trogh and I dashed into some old infantry foxholes about twenty-five yards away, along the road. A German 170 mm. shell had made a direct hit on a jeep carrying a major and his driver about forty feet away from us, tossing parts into the admission tent and riddling the tent with fragments. One of the guys in the jeep was just meat; the other had both legs and an arm blown off and lived about fifteen minutes. Two Thirty-second Field Hospital men were slightly wounded. Why a lot of us weren't killed, I don't know, except that the jeep had taken most of the force of the explosion. I didn't know a jeep could be so thoroughly demolished by anything. Division clearing station boys next door piled into their trucks and left in a great hurry. We soon followed. It was a wild ride in the blackout of the mountain with that crazy loon Tooney driving. I got the impression that he was trying to outrun any further shells. We are being put up by Colonel Blesse at the 56th Evac. I looked up Charlie Bussey and talked a couple of hours with him on professional subjects before turning in.

September 24, 1944—Thirty-second Field Hospital, Rifredo
Colonel Forsee returned from France yesterday and came up to the Fifty-sixth Evac to see us where we were hanging around waiting for the snarl to untangle. Colonel Patterson, the CO of the Thirty-second Field Hospital, who put us in the front line, surely does look sheepish. This afternoon we went back up to the crossroads disaster of yesterday afternoon, struck our tents, picked up our belongings and moved back

of the area about two miles to Rifredo. We took pictures of the mangled jeep that was hit yesterday. It rained all morning, and our old friend mud is everywhere again. This inexperienced Thirty-second Field Hospital outfit is lousy getting set up. I can see it isn't going to be good. We are behind a fairly high ridge and I think have some defilade here, thank heavens. I find myself a little jumpy; there is still plenty of shelling pretty close.

September 25, 1944—Thirty-second Field Hospital, Rifredo
We didn't start admitting patients until 12:00 noon, and even then things were not nearly ready. The trouble is that this outfit doesn't know what the essential stuff is to get it ready first. This afternoon Taylor and I walked up to the summit of the ridge in front of us and watched the war in the valley before us. Our guns were shelling heavily the mountains to the west, the north, and the northeast. I don't see how Jerry stays there, but he does, and only about five miles across the valley at that.

September 26, 1944—Thirty-second Field Hospital, Rifredo
I have an intestinal infection, the first I have had in over eighteen months, and I felt pretty lousy all day. Tonight I am plain sick. There is furious shelling on both sides in the valley before us. There is a continuous uproar from the guns firing and the shells exploding.

September 27, 1944—Thirty-second Field Hospital, Rifredo
It rained all day today, and it is miserably wet and cold. This Thirty-second Field Hospital doesn't seem to know much about a field setup. They still haven't trenched their tents, and water streams through the operating room and the ward tents constantly.

September 29, 1944—Thirty-second Field Hospital, Rifredo
More rain today. This is awful. Another platoon of the Thirty-second Field Hospital moved up above Firenzulo, so the boys are advancing; how, I don't see at all. This is very rugged country, and with this rain, I don't see how they fight at all. We did a German casualty early this morning who had a rectal wound, and the tents leaked merrily down on us the whole time.

September 30, 1944—Thirty-second Field Hospital, Rifredo
Today it didn't rain, and as we were off (although working until 3:30 A.M.), we decided to go to Florence. There is an amazing difference in the climate on this side of the Giorgo Pass as compared to the south

129

side. There is very little rain, and it is dusty and quite warm on the south side. We stopped by Headquarters, which is about eight miles north of Florence, and I picked up my winter clothing and put the finishing touches on my tourniquet paper. We went into Florence and ate dinner at the Excelsior Hotel. Pretty nice. Taylor, George Sehlinger, and I ordered and ate two entire meals. In the afternoon we went to the medical depot in Florence to replenish a very essential supply item—namely, 95 percent alcohol.

To our amazement, we were denied this vital substance. Colonel Forsee, the stinker, had left orders that no more alcohol was to be issued. We headed back out and ate supper at Voges's platoon of the Thirty-second Field Hospital. These folks were all excited about Bebe Daniels's visit and radio recording, which took place yesterday in this outfit.

October 2, 1944—Thirty-second Field Hospital, Rifredo
Today is my birthday, I guess. I had a recurrence of the gastrointestinal trouble today and felt pretty lousy. It rained all day again.

October 3, 1944—Rifredo
We officially closed down today. It was clear and sunny all day, for a change. Tonight they put in a call for three teams to go up to help out in the Second platoon of the Thirty-second Field, who are flooded with casualties, mostly Schu mine amputations. The hospital is up near Firenzuola. The German air force put on a show tonight, bombing and strafing up near Firenzuola. We could plainly see the tracers coming down in streaks while they were strafing. We got some casualties from it here, but had to send them along since we were closed down. This is the first air raid I have seen close up since we were below Rome.

October 5, 1944—Thirty-second Field Hospital, Rifredo
Taylor was pulled over to the Thirty-third Field Hospital today. My team went up to the Second Platoon near Firenzuola and spent four hours on a guy with extremity wounds, and what wounds they were. I can't get over what the tiny little pieces of mortar fragments do to the underlying tissue once the fragments get through the skin. Jim Mason, of Birmingham, Alabama, does very nice work indeed.

October 6, 1944—Thirty-second Field Hospital, Guignola
Just after lunch today, the CO of the Thirty-second Field Hospital came in to tell us we were to move to the First Platoon, to a place on a temporary road called Belvidere. It was about eighteen miles by road,

although only eight by airline, and the road (No. 6529) was very bad, being little more than a mud track. Of course, it had to be pouring down rain while we were loading and part of the way up. We kept going and going; finally, after having lost Trogh in the truck and having to wait a long time for him to catch up, it began to get dark. I saw a medical outfit in a little town and stopped to ask about the situation. It was a collecting station of the Eighty-fifth Division, and the captain in charge assured me that there was no field hospital or clearing station up ahead, as the front was only three or four miles away. Well, my map, which I had carefully marked before starting, said to go on, so on we went, with some trepidation on my part. Another two miles brought us to the Eighty-eighth Division Clearing Station, which was just moving in at Guignola. We went on and found the First platoon mired down in a field. They had their four main tents up, but nothing else. It was pouring rain again, and as we had borrowed a truck from the Third Platoon of the Thirty-second Field Hospital, we had to unload it in the dark and rain. We managed to pitch one tent after a fashion and lug our stuff in, using strict blackout. Boy! Was I tired! After that, we all slept in the ward tents—enlisted men, nurses, and officers wherever they could find a place to put a cot. Jim Mason and Stokes Monroe showed up about 8:30 P.M., very depressed over the whole situation. We are in front of all the artillery and can plainly hear mortars, machine guns, and our own shells bursting on a hill a couple of miles north of us. What a spot! And what a night!

October 7, 1944—Thirty-second Field Hospital, Guignola
This isn't good. The front lines are only a couple of miles away, and Jerry shells are whining over our heads going south while our shells are ripping the air over us going north. We watched a barrage laid down by us on the hill at the head of this valley. I hope Jerry doesn't decide to do some retaliation on medical installations just now. Started admitting patients at 8:00 A.M. and started operating at noon. Worked steadily until 12:00 midnight. Frank Hall's team came up today, as did Colonel Eldridge Campbell, the chief neurosurgeon in the Mediterranean theater. We are working three operating tables constantly and the going is tough. There are always plenty of casualties behind this Eighty-eighth Division. The mud and slush are terrific now, and it rains most of the time.

October 8, 1944—Thirty-second Field Hospital, Guignola
We started working at 4:00 P.M. today and worked until 8:00 A.M. the next morning. Colonel Forsee came up and stayed around, watching

for quite a while tonight. He is very jovial and nice these days. He brought some letters from my wife, thank heavens. Two batteries of 155 Howitzers are just on the other side of the road from us. I hope there is no counterbattery fire.

October 9, 1944—Thirty-second Field Hospital, Guignola
Still working awfully hard. In fact, it is hard to keep the days straight. We worked sixteen hours, fall in bed, get up in eight hours, and do postoperative care, and repeat this process. Howard Snyder has been up the past two days working with Lt. Col. Eldridge Campbell. Colonel Campbell is surgical chief of the Thirty-second General Hospital and a well-known neurosurgeon. He is a swell fellow and a good surgeon, although somewhat new and slow at the type of cases we are handling. We give him all the head wounds to do, but, of course, these casualties have a good many other wounds, which he is forced to take care of. I will have to get Charlie Bussey straightened out when I see him again. According to Campbell, Charlie Bussey told him to be sure to watch me work as I was one of the best surgeons in Italy! I never realized Charlie was such an exaggerater!

October 10, 1944—Thirty-second Field Hospital, Guignola
When will they learn not to put hospitals so far forward? We worked from 4:00 P.M. until 8:00 A.M., and I was exhausted. After eating breakfast, I went over into the supply tent to do a postmortem on one of my patients. About the time I finished, three shells landed in the area, shrapnel whined around, and I decided I had seen enough on the postmortem. It was bilateral pneumonia. We could hear a lot of screaming going on a short distance off, and pretty soon they started lugging about fifteen wounded men who were bleeding, moaning, and groaning. The shells had hit among the Nineteenth Engineers, who were bivouacked just across the road from us and were lined up being issued winter clothing. Three shells dropped right into the group. I went and helped out in the shock tent, feeling very exposed the whole time. After things were straightened out, I started digging myself a foxhole, but found I was too tired to do it, so I went out into the fields and found a Paesano to dig it for me. He finished about 4:00 P.M. and then worked on Trogh's tent foxhole. We sunk our cots below ground. I went to bed right after supper and slept through until morning without waking once.

October 13, 1944—Thirty-second Field Hospital
We are still getting a lot of wounded in. The Eighty-eighth Division boys seem to be about the only outfit gaining, but they are paying a

132

heavy price. The Germans are fighting hard and bringing up reinforcements constantly. Everyone figured that they would pull out after we broke through the Gothic Line at Giorgo Pass, but they haven't quit by any means. I am not superstitious, but I am glad to see this day pass.

October 14, 1944—Thirty-second Field Hospital, Guignola

It rained all day again. We were starting to do a case when Beech, who is living in our tent, rushed in all out of breath, gasping that his foxhole had caved in on his bed and our foxholes were filling up with water. The patient was just being induced by anesthesia, so Trogh and I rushed over and pulled our cots out of the holes, with much muddying of everything. Oh me! We then returned and did the surgical case.

October 16, 1944—Thirty-second Field Hospital, Guignola

The American Board of Surgery written examination, which I applied to take, is due in nine days, and I haven't studied a lick. Just too tired and too busy.

October 17, 1944—Thirty-second Field Hospital, Guignola

The Eighty-eighth Division put on a drive today to take Mount Grande, which is supposed to be the last high hill before the Po Valley. It was clear today, and we went up on a hill and watched our Thunderbirds bomb the whole mountain with incendiary bombs and other bombs. We have been under direct observation from this mountain right along, and I believe the Jerries really do respect the Red Cross.

October 18, 1944—Thirty-second Field Hospital, Guignola

I started studying for my exam today. Colonel Forsee had sent a "Best and Taylor" physiology book and a "McCallum" pathology. I went through about a third of the physiology book.

Octoer 19, 1944—Thirty-second Field Hospital, Guignola

Rain and more rain. More mud and more mud. We moved our tent a couple of days back up into a cornfield and put up a stove, which we finally got. Not so bad in the tent now.

October 20, 1944—Guignola

The infantry boys took Mount Grande okay, but they have been bogged down since. Studied some more. The colonel was up today and told me to come back to Headquarters on the twenty-third to prepare for the examination of the American Board of Surgery. I am still not feeling well—poor food, poor appetite and intermittent diarrhea.

October 23, 1944—Headquarters, ten miles north of Florence

I got Scotty and Burns to bring me back to Headquarters today in our truck. That damn road (No. 6529) gets worse right along, and the engineers work on it constantly day and night. Chains are an absolute necessity to get over it. It was pretty cold, and the MPs made Scotty take off his chains at Radicosa Pass where we hit Highway No. 65. This job got Scotty muddy from head to foot, besides producing a lot of cussing. Headquarters is located in a nice grassy spot surrounded by pine woods. There is a palpable lessening of tension this far back.

October 24, 1944—Headquarters, ten miles north of Florence

Henry Hoffman and Tom Ballentine came in this morning for the examinations that Reeve Betts was to give us for the American Board of Surgery. We studied all afternoon, then went to Florence tonight to see Catherine Cornell and Brian Aherne in *The Barretts of Wimpole Street* at the Apollo. It was really very nice. There were a number of GIs who did not appreciate the stage and walked out early, but those that remained were held spellbound at times, even all coughing ceasing. A wild ride home thereafter—Tom had some trouble with his jeep, and, going on the theory that a speed below forty miles per hour would lead to inevitable disaster, we arrived home very quickly.

October 25, 1944—Headquarters, north of Florence

It was a hell of an examination. I wrote at top speed for six hours and at that forgot to put down a lot of stuff I knew. Oh, well! Went into Florence again tonight. Went to dinner out at the Twenty-fourth General Hospital. Boy! would I like to be in the general hospital this winter!

October 26, 1944—Headquarters

Colonel Forsee returned from a trip to Naples and told us to spend another day here. So we piled into Tom's jeep and went to Florence. Tom got a couple of nice Red Cross workers, Helena Day and Eleanor Bailey, to help us shop, which they did. The merchandise that we saw was not anything to write home about, but I bought a few things. In the afternoon, we rode out to see Tom's wife's tutor, Mme. Consuella. She lived in a lovely home and was a charming person. Also went over the Arno to see Michelangelo's *David*. Then to tea at a real clip joint. Dinner at the Excelsior, and home around ten.

October 27, 1944—A Platoon, Thirty-second Field Hospital, Guignola

Back to the old grind. Fortunately, all my patients did well while I was gone. Another thoroughly miserable day—rain, wind, and sleet.

134

Captain Whalen, CO of B Platoon of the Thirty-third Field Hospital, did me a real favor in loaning me his jeep to get back over this horrible road labeled No. 6529.

October 28, 1944—Thirty-second Field Hospital, Guignola
Things are pretty quiet. Jim Mason pulled one that caused us a lot of mirth. He had this patient with a transection of the spinal cord produced by a missile in the dorsal region. Trogh overheard the following conversation:
"How do you feel?"
"I hurt all over."
"Well, you can't hurt all over. Where do you hurt?"
"Everywhere."
"Well, does your hair hurt?," in a very aggrieved tone.
"No."
"Do your fingernails hurt?"
"No."
"Do your toenails hurt?"
"No."
"Well, you don't hurt all over. Where do you hurt?"
"Everywhere."
Trying a new approach, Jim started pinching the boy below the transection level. Jim: "Does this hurt?" Patient: "What?" Not getting anywhere with this line of thought, Jim tried moving the toes. "Which way am I raising and moving your toes?" Patient, raising his head and looking: "Up." Jim, thoroughly exasperated: "No, no! Don't look, just tell me what I'm doing." Patient, raising his head again and looking: "Moving my toe." The utter futility of the whole thing was too much for Jim, so Trogh had been going around yelling at Jim, "Hey, Jim, does your hair hurt?"

October 29, 1944—Thirty-second Field Hospital, Guignola
Amputated the thigh of an awfully nice boy today, this boy being from Richmond, Virginia. Taylor threw a party tonight, which ended as a singing session. Beech and Sturm have nice voices. We were particularly effective, or so we thought, on "I Walked in the Garden Alone." Some people didn't appreciate it at 2:00 A.M., I'm afraid.

October 31, 1944—Thirty-second Field Hospital, Guignola
Colonel Forsee was up today and told Jim and me to come back to Headquarters in a few days. I, for one, am ready to go. Don't know whether it is physical or mental, but I tire more easily than I used to

and hate to see a case come in. It rains every day without fail. Mud is everywhere—in our beds, in our food, all over our clothes—and it gets steadily worse. Wonder what it will feel like to go without galoshes?

November 3, 1944—Headquarters, ten miles north of Florence
It was raining again this morning, and Trogh was not easily persuaded to get up. However, we went ahead and got things ready to leave. Jim Mason's team is going back with us. Had to lug everything about 100 yards because this mud made it impossible to get the trucks in our area. Jim, Joe Lawrence, Mike Weston, and I decided to ride in the back of the truck, which had no top. An ambulance was available, but I didn't want the headache an ambulance gives me. Well, we hadn't gone a mile before it began to rain. Just before we hit Futa Pass, it began to rain like the very devil, with hail and high winds. Naturally, we all got thoroughly soaked, and arrived at Headquarters wet and very cold.

November 4, 1944—Headquarters, ten miles north of Florence
We were alerted last night, and this morning Jim Mason, Sorehead Poole, and I drew lots to see who would go up to Montecatina to set up with a platoon of the Thirty-second Field Hospital. It seems that the Thirty-eighth Evac at Pisa, which had set up nicely on the flat ground next to the Arno, was under six feet of water and naturally were taking no patients. They are sending this platoon of the Thirty-second to take up the slack on the wounded. Well, Jim, the poor devil, lost. George Stevenson was the other team that had to go. You could hear Joe Lawrence, Jim Mason's anesthetist, crying from a distance of a mile.

November 6, 1944—Florence
Today was a nice day, for a wonder, and we helped move Headquarters into Florence. The colonel has shown a lot of sense in his selection of the site. We have taken over the Institute of Hygiene, located on Via Morgagni, which is part of the University of Florence. This Institute of Hygiene is in a modern building, with good plumbing, lights, most of the windows, and no heat. It surely is a relief to get out of the mud!

November 9, 1944—Headquarters, Florence
Went out to the Twenty-fourth General today and met Ben Colcock. He is a very stimulating person, and it was a pleasure to make rounds with him and see some of our mistakes. I found six of my patients all going well. Ben and I see eye to eye on most things, especially double barrel colostomies.

136

November 10, 1944—Headquarters, Florence

Jim Mason, Larry Hunt, and I went to a meeting of all the surgical chiefs at the Twenty-fourth General Hospital, where Churchill had debates on various topics. We had a wonderful steak dinner, and the discussions were very good. Ben Colcock defended double barrel colostomy in an excellent fashion.

November 11, 1944—Florence

Today is Armistice Day, but there is no armistice here. It seems that I am to go into the hospital for a checkup. Haven't been feeling very well for some time and have lost some weight. Thought I had better get this occasional diarrhea checked while I am doing nothing. Bill Bowers, one of our great anesthesiologists, is going in as a patient, too.

November 13, 1944—Twenty-fourth General Hospital, Florence

We checked in yesterday afternoon, and things started with a bang. A Major Archinard is my doctor. Stool check this A.M. and proctoscopy this P.M. This proctoscopy was the first I had ever had done; it was not too bad, but no fun.

November 14, 1944—Twenty-fourth General Hospital, Florence

Nothing found in the examinations done yesterday. I am ambulatory and go to the mess hall, where the food is good.

November 15, 1944—Twenty-fourth General Hospital, Florence

Well, they claimed to have found some endamebic cysts today, so I am going to have to stay around another ten days for a course of Carbasone. I read a book a day. Bill Bowers was certainly knocked for a loop by Scopolamine and Nembutal given for lipiodol study of his lungs. He was out cold for about four hours and lost all conception of time and space. During his recovery, we in the ward got a lot of laughs out of questioning him regarding his sexual life, his opinion of various people, et cetera. He gave us straight answers because he had had what amounted to a "truth serum."

November 17, 1944—Twenty-fourth General Hospital, Florence

Bill Bowers got out today; nothing wrong. I am still doing nothing but reading and shooting the breeze. Glen Gummess is a patient here with hepatitis, and Pat Imes from the Thirty-eighthh Evac is also a patient. Lieutenant Colonel Brewton of Asheville, CO of the 313 Medics, is here waiting to go home. He had a severe pneumococcal meningitis, but is apparently entirely recovered except for a diplopia.

November 18, 1944—Twenty-fourth General Hospital, Florence

A dull life. Took a walk along the Arno, but with the "Danger, Schu Mines" signs everywhere, did little diverging from the straight and narrow way.

November 20, 1944—Twenty-fourth General Hospital, Florence

I have been going up and watching Ben Colcock and other men do secondary closures, skin grafts, et cetera. Watched Charbonnet do a lung decortication today. It seemed to work okay.

November 22, 1944—Twenty-fourth General Hospital, Florence

Tomorrow is Thanksgiving over here, and I have arranged to go back to Headquarters for dinner. This afternoon, I went down to the Verdi Theater and saw *The Barber of Seville*. Very good, especially the orchestra and the ballet dancing by the daughter of Nijinski.

November 23, 1944—Twenty-fourth General Hospital, Florence

Went back to Headquarters for noon dinner. Broke out my liquor ration and invited the boys in. The bottle of whiskey lasted about ten minutes, but with enough effect for the serenading of the dining hall with "When the War is Over" et cetera. The meal was excellent. Came back out here just in time to eat another Thanksgiving dinner in the evening, but really couldn't do justice to it.

December 1, 1944—Headquarters, Florence

On November 26, I finally persuaded Major Archinard to let me go back to Headquarters. The colonel is still in France.

Through a complicated process, we have been invited by Professor Pietro Valdoni to visit him at the Baselewski Clinic. This morning, we went to this clinic and found Peiro Frugoni there also. It seems that Peiro had come up here in order to get various papers of vital nature so he could get married. He is marrying this wealthy Jewish gal that we met in Rome—I forget her name. Peiro is still doing no work, and I doubt if he ever does enough to amount to much professionally. We watched Valdoni, who is professor of surgery at the University of Florence and a rather young man (forty-two, I believe), do a bone graft for a Pott's disease of the spine. He takes very thin osteoperiosteal graft from the tibia under local and, still under local, cuts down and splits the opposite lamina for his graft bed. His results on X rays, which he showed us, are very good. He uses this type of graft for all kinds of bridging of lesions, its chief advantage being that it is malleable.

December 4, 1944—Headquarters, Florence

Went down to see Valdoni work again. He did three gastric resections, averaging about forty-five minutes each. He does them all under local anesthesia, gets the patient out of bed the next day, starts oral fluids the next day. He practically never has to resort to parenteral fluids or gastric suction drainage. It is all very amazing. He does a posterior Polya type of anastomosis without clamps, no-loop type. He states that he has had one death in the last three hundred cases. I went around with him and saw his postoperative patients. None looked as if they had undergone a major surgical procedure. I believe his success is due to (1) local anesthesia, (2) no clamps, (3) not very extensive ulcer disease. He insists that one must get below the ulcer in the duodenum to have a successful operation. Well, I am going to have to see more of this.

December 5, 1944—Headquarters, Florence

Professor Valdoni invited Tommy Emmi, George Hopkins, George Stephenson, and me to his home to dinner tonight (Via Zara No. 7). We took along a bunch of candy and stuff for the kids and a few other provisions. The kids are five in number and very nice. Mrs. Valdoni is quite young and pretty. The dinner was very nice, served quite elaborately, with wines, liqueurs, and all the rest. It is very pleasant to eat in such an atmosphere again. Valdoni is surely enthusiastic about his work.

December 6, 1944—Headquarters, Florence

On this day, Colonel Churchill addressed the Southern Surgical Association at White Sulphur Springs, West Virginia. In his talk he said, "Among the forward surgeons of the Auxiliary Surgical Group are Luther Wolff, Larry Hunt, Jim Mason, Gene Colwell, Paul Dent, Dan Williams, and many others. These men not only exhibit loyalty and devotion but treat GI Joe with the same sense of responsibility they might show to private patients at home."

December 7, 1944—Headquarters, Florence

Pearl Harbor Day! Three years ago I never thought things would be like this. Looks like a long war, and it isn't a cheerful prospect.

December 9, 1944—Headquarters, Florence

The Christmas packages are beginning to roll in. I got five tonight, mostly from Mary Will, filled with fine food. It sure is a help, but the letter situation is atrocious.

December 12, 1944—Headquarters, Florence

I went up to Correggi Hospital, which is near here, to watch Valdoni work. He insisted on my scrubbing with him on a gastric resection, which I did, acting as his first assistant. Things went okay and he paid me the compliment of saying it was like I had been working with him for five years.

December 13, 1944—Headquarters, Florence

Went downtown today and to this jewelry store, which makes bracelets and so forth and is quite reputable. I decided to get a chrysophase bracelet and ring for Mary Will. I thought they were quite pretty, although it is always questionable whether my thoughts amount to anything along these lines.

December 14, 1944—Headquarters, Florence

These friends of Tony Emmi invited Steve, Hopkins, Alex Little, and me together with Tony to a dinner tonight. It was very nice, and we had a good time, although Tony and Alex got a little drunk. The furniture at this home would have driven an antique collector crazy. It was lovely and very old.

December 15, 1944—Headquarters, Florence

Valdoni left a note for me to come up and do a case, which I did this morning. Gastric resections are rather simple if done with his technique. It took me almost an hour, but I guess I wasn't too bad; at least the professor seemed to think it was okay.

December 17, 1944—Headquarters, Florence

Enough boxes of food came for the four men in my room (Trogh, Hopkins, Tony, and me) to require five men to carry them up. I got thirteen packages today. We have very fine wives; at least, I am sure I do.

December 20, 1944—Headquarters, Florence

The patient I operated on for Valdoni is doing okay. Valdoni invited Henry Hoffman, Frank Hall, and me to dinner tonight. Also a Lt. Col. Bob Forsythe, who is with the South African hospital and on the surgical staff of Capetown University. It was a very pleasant evening. The Valdoni kids are cute, and they are beginning to think I am Santa Claus, with my pockets stuffed with *caramelli*.

December 21, 1944—Headquarters, Florence

I took Ben Colcock down to the Baselewski Clinic to see Valdoni work. I then had him here to lunch. He seemed to enjoy it a lot and was duly impressed.

December 23, 1944—Headquarters, Florence
The weather has cleared and has turned very cold. News from the First Army front is anything but good, with the German counteroffensive proceeding right along (Battle of the Bulge).

December 25, 1944—Headquarters, Florence
Had a very nice dinner and all the turkey we could eat. Stephenson and Alex Little had predinner open house, and four quarts of whiskey disappeared in a hurry. Tonight we had a party here. Most of the nurses had imported dates, so Tony invited a number of Italian girls, which helped a lot. The whole affair had the atmosphere of a nightclub, and almost everyone seemed to enjoy themselves. But it just wasn't Christmas for me.

December 28, 1944—Headquarters, Italy
Trogh, assigned to Larry Hunt's team, and Stephenson were sent over to the 170th Evac this morning because Jerry put on a slight push above Lucia. I visited all the Evacs (Eighth, Fifteenth, Sixteenth, Thirty-eighth, Ninety-fourth, Fifty-sixth and 170th) about three weeks ago collecting statistics on gas infections. The Eighth and Ninety-fourth Evacs are up toward the front on Highway 65.

December 31, 1944—Headquarters, Florence
About 10:00 P.M. most of us gathered in a back room for eats and drinks in celebration of New Year's Eve. Joe Finegold had acquired some noisemakers and confetti, which we used with enthusiasm. About midnight, we went down to the enlisted men's stag party and had a song session, each striving to outyell the other. Tony, Joe Finegold, and I came up about 2:30 A.M., woke all the guys, wished them a Happy New Year, and dumped confetti in their faces. Some fun, no doubt.

January 1, 1945—Headquarters, Florence
We had a nice turkey dinner and then went to a football game at the municipal stadium between the Fifth Army and Twelfth Air Force. Every effort was made to get the effects of a football game back home, floats, bands, cheerleaders, beauty queen, mascots, and all the rest. It was a beautiful day for football. Fifth Army sort of outclassed the Air Force, beating them 20 to 0.

January 9, 1945—Headquarters, Florence

Colonel Forsee called me down to inform me that my tourniquet paper was wanted for publication in the army *Medical Bulletin.* It puts me in a quandary. I don't want it published there, but don't see how I can very gracefully refuse. I plan to go to Leghorn tomorrow to talk it over with Mike Mason, whom I would like to see anyhow.

January 11, 1945—Headquarters, Florence

Had a nice trip to Leghorn today to see Mike Mason and Harvey Allen, who are stationed with the Twelfth General Hospital. The Twelfth General Hospital recently moved up to a nice location between Leghorn and Marina di Pisa. Mike Mason is a full colonel and in command of the Twelfth General, and Harvey Allen is chief of surgery of the Twelfth General. They are swell fellows whom I had known quite a while in Chicago and are very friendly. Mike Mason went over my problem with my paper and seemed somewhat puzzled as to what to do. He finally advised sending it in to *Surgery, Gynecology and Obstetrics,* but in view of the difficulties and uncertainties, I have decided to say okay to the bulletin and let it go at that. *Shortly after my paper, "Tourniquet Problems in War Injuries," was published in the bulletin of the Army Medical Department, No. 87, April, 1945, a directive came out from the Army Medical Department drastically changing the handling of tourniquets in wounds of the extremities. These changes are certainly a little late, but I am sure that some lives will be saved by these changes.*

Glen Gummess and Mike Mason went with me on this trip, and as they had never seen Pisa, we came back and they persuaded me to walk up the Leaning Tower again!

January 15, 1945—Florence, Italy

I spent the whole afternoon and evening working on the arduous task of gathering together all the abdominal cases that had been done by the Second Auxiliary Surgical Group and trying to arrange them in some sort of order. I had to plan the methods to be used, the charts to be drawn, and the general format to be utilized. It is going to be one hell of a job, and I don't mean perhaps. I probably will be screaming to go back into the field in a couple of weeks, although even at present I am still perfectly content to spend this winter in this lovely building— that is, lovely as compared to a pyramidal tent.

January 19, 1945—Florence, Italy

I worked all morning on these damned case records until 3:00 P.M., when Tom Ballentine and I went out to the villa of this Madam Consuella, the former tutor of Tom's wife, to a bridge party. It was a mixed party. These Italians take their bridge very seriously, and there was much unintelligible (to me) jabbering after each hand. They play very well but do not play a very aggressive type of bridge and take very few chances. These people are mostly middle-age married couples, the upper social strata, and very ultra polite in culture, but don't impress me as being too strong characters when it comes to getting things done except having a good time.

January 21, 1945—Florence, Italy

I felt pretty darn lucky today. Tom Ballentine and Sturm had to go on a sixty-mile trip this morning to testify in a court-martial, and as it was a nice day, I thought I would go along, but decided I had better spend the day working on these reports instead. Well, Tom thinks there are only two speeds while driving a jeep: full ahead and stop. They ran under the back end of a truck while going down the road and emerged only with minor lacerations and contusions, which was indeed very fortunate.

February 5, 1945—Headquarters, Florence, Italy

Well, it seems I passed the American Board of Surgeons, Part I, satisfactorily and won't have to worry about that any more. I am certainly not going to worry about Part II, which I can't take until I get back to the States anyhow. I'll worry about it then.

February 8, 1945—Headquarters, Florence, Italy

We've been having some wonderful weather lately. Clear, crisp days with a definite hint of spring in the atmosphere. As you probably have noticed, I haven't written about the weather nearly so much since I have been back to Headquarters. Weather just isn't that important an item as it is out in the field. For instance, when the moon is up, in the field it isn't necessary to carry a flashlight. Rain, however, necessitates keeping the tent flaps down and the tents closed, which means darkness all day long inside except for a dim candlelight. In other words, one just naturally notices weather a lot more while in the field.

February 9, 1945—Headquarters, Florence

We worked all morning and until 3:30 this afternoon checking on the abdominal cases. Glen Gummess and I usually take a walk in the afternoon, practicing our so-called Italian, on the natives who love to try to correct our pronounciation. This afternoon we went up a hill about two miles from here, saw an interesting-looking gate set in an extensive high wall, and decided to inspect the place. I attracted the attention of a Paesano on the other side of the gate, entered it as if it belonged to us, and found one of the most beautiful places I have ever seen over here. This tremendous, palatial estate has statues, formal gardens, winding bridal paths, lakes, waterfalls, vistas and what have you. I have no earthly idea as to whom it belongs, but we enjoyed looking it over and acting as if we owned the place.

February 10, 1945—Headquarters, Florence, Italy
Well, it looks as if Red Robby, Glen Gummess, and I will be taking off for this very highbrow British surgical congress that is being held back in Rome. There are only a few representatives entitled to go, and the three highest ranking officers here at Headquarters are invited, which are we three. It should be quite nice, all in all, and certainly I couldn't ask to go with two nicer fellows than Robby and Glen.

February 11, 1945—Rome, Italy
This is a little bit of all right! We made a very uneventful flight down from Florence, going out over the sea. We are really nicely fixed up as far as accommodations are concerned, being in the Excelsior Hotel, in which I stayed during the two previous trips to Rome. We three have a nice suite consisting of two bedrooms, a bath, and a sitting room. I don't know how we happened to rate all of this, but we are not complaining. Rome itself is much quieter than previously. There is not quite the air of rush and bustle nor the dusty field uniforms, helmets, and weapons et cetera to be seen. Everyone dresses quite correctly, and the war seems a very long distance away.

This meeting sounds like it will be very good. All the chiefs of surgery from the American hospitals are attending and, of course, all the surgeons from the British, Canadian, South African, and New Zealand outfits and hospitals that can be spared. We are counting on Robby to do right by us. As mentioned previously, Robby worked with the British in a casualty clearing station during the whole period of Anzio, and besides doing a good job, he became very good friends with them. About a month ago he was made an honorary member of the British army and was awarded the decoration Order of the British Empire, which is quite an honor. So we figured we could bask in his reflected glory and maybe get a few shots of Scotch out of it. We will be here almost a week more or less, since the meeting continues until next Saturday. Subsequent plans are very vague at the present time.

February 12, 1945—Rome, Italy
The meeting, which officially started this morning and ran

throughout the day, was very excellent. These Britishers have a command of the English language and the poise and clarity of presentation that the average American just doesn't possess, and it is a real pleasure to hear them talk about things, even if one knows all about everything that is said.

We have just returned from a reception at the British embassy, which was a very highbrow affair, but a bit disappointing in the drinks. They had some sort of horrible punch instead of the Scotch that we had anticipated.

February 14, 1945—Rome, Italy

This morning's activities warrant a more or less detailed description, I think, for in spite of being a non-Catholic, I was very much impressed.

It was announced that we could take a tour of the Vatican and have an audience with the pope (Pope Pius XII) if we so desired. Inasmuch as I haven't seen a good part of the Vatican, including the Sistine Chapel and the Vatican Museum, I decided to go and have a look. Well, it turned out that it was an experience that I wouldn't have cared to miss. We were met by an official English-speaking guide. (When I say "we" I mean the 150-odd delegates here at the surgical congress.) We were taken all through Saint Peter's, and a great many interesting things were explained to us that I had missed entirely on my previous short trip. We were then conducted into the pope's living quarters to the right of the main entrance of Saint Peter's. The balcony from which the pope usually addresses the public is part of this building. The Swiss guards that are all over the place literally have to be seen to be believed. They have costumes of brilliant white, blue, and red stripes, with medieval-looking steel helmets, pikes, and spears. Various other military-looking characters with the most unique and colorful costumes appeared from time to time with an intermittent display of formally dressed gentlemen in full dress, tails, each wearing variegated cummerbunds. We finally wound up in a sort of reddish room and waited for the pope to appear; this he did after a bit. He is a very frail-looking personage with an ascetic face from which peer alert and kindly eyes. He had a tremendously impressive personality, with wisdom and suffering and understanding showing through. I am sure no one could help having a great deal of respect for him. He made us a very nice talk, a copy of which I am sending home. He speaks English quite well, although with an accent. Apparently he knows almost all ordinary languages, since I heard him speak Polish to a couple of Polish surgeons next to me. Well, we got in line and he shook hands and spoke to each one of us, asking where we were from. When I thanked him for his address to us, he said to me, "Thank you and a very special blessing on you." This, I understand, is quite something: to have him give you his very special blessing in person. He gave each of us, after shaking hands (the Catholics kissed his ring), a medal and his picture. This medal is supposed to confer "plenary indulgence" and has certain other features of significance. The pope's hand felt very feverish, and he looked quite sick. I felt sorry for him for having made himself go through all that he did, when obviously he should have been in bed. After he left, giving us his benediction, Glen and I walked over to one of the formally dressed gentlemen who seemed to be in charge of the medal department and asked him what the medal meant. He said, "No capito" (Don't understand) and handed us another medal, which we took.

After the audience with the pope, we went through the museum, which had many priceless paintings and other works of art, and through the Sistine Chapel. I was a trifle · disappointed in the latter. Michelangelo's works weren't quite what I expected, possibly because they had been praised excessively by people who had seen them before or maybe just because I am not too much of an art critic.

The meeting this afternoon was very interesting, being on abdominal surgery. We handle these injuries a great deal like the British, with one or two notable exceptions.

February 16, 1945—Rome
I called Pierre Frugoni this morning, and he invited me, Charlie Bussey, and a Canadian surgeon, Dr. Ganshorn, who was first assistant when I was at the Mayo Clinic, to his apartment for dinner. We had a real Mayo Clinic reunion. Pierre has married this girl since I last saw him in Florence. He seemed more like his old self than at any time I have seen him. His wife speaks excellent English and is quite wealthy, I understand. The dinner was very good, but I don't feel just right about going out to dinner with civilians, because about all the food is black market stuff, which is sold at terrific prices, but I assume the wife can afford it.

February 17, 1945—Rome
The meeting ended this morning with a gathering of all the Americans under Dr. Churchill, our surgical consultant. We compared results with our British colleagues on various professional subjects. We are very proud of Dr. Churchill since he presented material with a great deal of facility and even surpassed a good many of the British in his

146

presentation. It was supposed to last only an hour but lasted three hours, so we missed our plane back to Florence. Glen Gummess and I arranged for a jeep and took a hurried tour of some of the more spectacular sights of the town, including art exhibits, ruins, tombs, churches, catacombs, and what not. It was a wonderful day, and I enjoyed it all.

February 18, 1945—Rome

We went to the airport early this morning, boarded our C-47 plane, flew up the coast to the Arno River, and so to Florence. Fortunately, Florence is pretty well socked in with weather, so we had to fly back. We are now staying in a very nice hotel, the air force hotel, which is a lot quieter and less of a rat race than the Excelsior. Incidentally, Doris Day and one of the Hutton heiresses, not Barbara, are staying here, too. They are supposed to be doing some sort of social work, which is a fine thing, no doubt, but the details of their social work are far from clear.

February 19, 1945—Rome, Italy

Went out to the airport again this morning and were told there was no space for us. We returned to this fine air force hotel. This actually didn't displease us too much, for there is every reason to enjoy the fine food, beds, and service. I imagine it will be quite some time before another similar chance occurs. The group here consists of Glen Gummess, Red Robby, Ben Colcock, C. B. Carter, and Frank Cox, and they are all a swell bunch of fellows. They are very entertaining and all interested in most things. Colcock is chief of surgery with the Twenty-fourth General Hospital in Florence, C. B. Carter is chief of surgery with the Fifty-sixth Evac Hospital, and Frank Cox is chief of surgery in one of the general hospitals. It seems quite clear that C. B. Carter has something to do with our remaining here in Rome. He has a relative who is in charge of the local air transportation, and it seems certain that he calls this relative every morning and tells him that we want to stay another day here in Rome.

February 20, 1945—Rome, Italy

C. B. Carter is still working his racket to keep us here in Rome. It seems that there is just no room in any transport plane going to Florence. I met a fairly high-ranking officer, a major general, from Washington tonight. His concept of the war is sure a long way from reality—so far, in fact, that at first I thought he was kidding when he made his remarks, but apparently he wasn't.

February 21, 1945—Florence, Italy

Today was quite a day. We left Rome this morning and flew up to Florence after having been kicked off flights for four days running because of C. B. Carter's arrangements. I didn't feel quite right being AWOL, in spite of the fact that there was nothing that we could do about it. We had a nice trip back, as it was a beautiful, sunny day. When I got back to headquarters the colonel called me in and told me that I had been awarded the Legion of Merit. This is a pretty high award, being below the Distinguished Service Cross and above the Silver Star. I feel a little ashamed about the whole matter, because there are a couple of dozen guys in this outfit who deserve it as much or more than I. I just got in on this war surgery a bit earlier than most of the others and have to thank old Trogh for writing it up for me. Three others have gotten the same decoration in our outfit, namely, Jim Sullivan, Jim Mason, and Reeve Betts, and I am sure eventually others will receive it. It means little except that all such awards will presumably count on points toward getting priority in going home, and in this respect I am all for it. The second thing that I was informed of when I got to Headquarters was that I was to get my stuff together at once to go up to the Thirty-second Field Hospital and to Valdiburo, which is backing up the Tenth Mountain Division. This Tenth Mountain Division is a crackerjack outfit just recently put in the line. A new wrinkle has developed, however: I am going without my team, but am going with the title of "Chief of Surgical Service." This is a new system they are trying out, making it a full-time, nonoperative job. It doesn't suit me a bit, but I was the only guy available, so I guess I am stuck, temporarily, at least. I haven't failed to point out to the colonel that I want to get back to operating.

February 22, 1945—Thirty-second Field Hospital, Valdiburo, Italy

This platoon is set up in a tiny village consisting of only half a dozen houses about four miles south of Poretto, which is a bigger town. The Tenth Mountain Division is ahead of us, as is Mount Belvidere, which is the highest peak in the vicinity and which apparently the Tenth Mountain is scheduled to take. The Brazilians are on our right flank, and I am not exactly sure who is on the left, if anybody. It seems that my duties are mostly to act as triage officer and arrange scheduling and assign cases to be done after working them up. The field hospital personnel have to be jacked up on occasion, and it is my duty to do so, unfortunately, which makes me somewhat of an SOB. Anyhow, I don't care whether inefficient people like me or not.

148

February 23, 1945—Valdiburo, Italy

We really have a gathering of great surgical talent in this platoon at the present time, and I feel very definitely foolish trying to act like a ."chief of surgery." The teams here are those of Reeve Betts, Larry Shefts, Henry Hoffman, George Stephenson, and Phil Giddings from the Second Aux. Charlie Rife, who is the best surgeon in the Ninety-fourth Evac, is here with his team. There are also two Brazilian surgical teams: one a Major Netto who is an excellent surgeon and professor of surgery at the University of São Paulo. The other Brazilian surgeon is not so hot. Personally, there is no animosity or resentment toward me whatsoever and they treat me with every consideration and courtesy. In fact, any one of these men might have been picked for the job of surgical chief; it just happened that I had no team at this time because Trogh went out with Larry Hurt's team and my anesthetist, Bess Barrett, went out with George Hopkins. I would much rather be working myself and have so informed the colonel.

It is very interesting working with these Brazilian surgeons, although there is some difficulty from the linguistic point of view. Only one or two members of these teams speak English. No patients speak English, so there is often much jabbering without much results, but the Brazilian doctors are all very nice and Professor Netto is really fine. I think he probably is a much better surgeon than most of us. Apparently in Brazil, postoperative care is something that is left entirely up to assistants and to the interns, and so we have had to do quite a job of suggesting and demonstrating in this regard. Now, however, things are going very well indeed and they have adopted our postoperative methods wholeheartedly and are giving surgical care every bit on a par with ours.

February 26, 1945—Valdiburo, Italy, Thirty-second Field Hospital

I am living in a tent with Charlie Rife and his assistant, Captain Sails, and an anesthetist, Captain Piezi. They are a nice bunch of fellows, particularly Charlie Rife, who is really a wonderful fellow and a superb surgeon. He practiced in Milwaukee and will unquestionably go far in the future. This tent life is some change from the fine hotels of Rome. In fact, that recent part of my life seems to be somewhat of a dream. The weather has been beautiful lately, too good to be true, almost. It is very cold in the morning up here in the mountains, but the days are quite pleasant. We have oil-burning stoves in our tents, and when they are burning it isn't half bad. There is not enough current from the portable generators for electric lights in the living tents, so we have to struggle along with the usual candles, oil lamps, and flashlights.

February 27, 1945—Thirty-second Field Hospital, Valdiburo, Italy

We weren't at all busy today, and as it was such a wonderful spring day, Henry Hoffman, Charlie Rife, and I decided to take a walk, leaving the hospital about 3:00 P.M. We walked about an hour and found out, upon our return, that a couple of generals had come by with their large entourages, looking for me. General Martin had a medal he wanted to pin on me and seemed quite upset that I was not present. Oh, well, I need my exercise.

February 28, 1945—Thirty-second Field Hospital, Valdiburo, Italy

Two years ago today, we had our last glimpse of the shoreline of the good old U.S.A. and started on this long, difficult absence. There is no point in crying over spilled milk, but I do very deeply regret the loss of these two years from my wife and children. This loss is certainly not compensated for by the adventures, excitement, and experiences I have gained in the war. Not by a long shot. Well, Gen. Joe Martin came up again this afternoon and pinned the Legion of Merit on me. Yesterday, he had brought along a lot of photographers and various other characters in his retinue and had planned to make a big presentation of this medal. Today, he came by himself with his jeep driver and the whole thing went off without any unnecessary fanfare, all of which I think is good. I shall send the medal home at the first chance I have, because I have a ribbon that is worn in lieu of the medal, although I haven't worn any ribbons at all since I came overseas. They seem a little ostentatious.

March 2, 1945—Thirty-second Field Hospital, Valdiburo, Italy

The Tenth Mountain Division pushed off today to take Mount Belvidere, and we really got to work in a big way. It seems that this job of mine is of some value in such a situation as this when we are rushed, mainly as a matter of coordination and making decisions as to which patients to do first, which ones can be safely evacuated, and keeping things moving. I do miss operating and intend to get back to it just as soon as they will let me.

March 3, 1945—Thirty-second Field Hospital, Valdiburo, Italy

We still are quite rushed and pushed even with six American surgical teams and two Brazilian teams working. This is twice as many teams as we usually have in a field hospital. The American teams

Gen. Joseph I. Martin (M.C.) awards me the Legion of Merit, Valdibura, Italy, February 28, 1945.

Citation for Legion of Merit

Luther H. Woff, 0-296324, Major, Medical Corps, 2nd Auxiliary Surgical Group, for exceptionally meritorious conduct in the performance of outstanding service in Italy from 9 September 1943 to 27 November 1944. Landing on the beach at Salerno, Italy with the initial assault forces, Major Wolff immediately organized the first medical installation in which major surgery was performed on the European continent. Despite numerous bombings and strafings, and meager facilities for performing such operations, Major Wolff, through his own resourcefulness, foresight, courage and apparent inexhaustible efforts in procuring and improvising the necessary supplies and equipment, combined with his outstanding surgical knowledge and skill, enabled the many severely wounded to receive excellent surgical care during the first days of the initial invasion of the Italian mainland. Major Wolff's efficient management in adopting and improvising needed facilities permitted the performance of major operations with an amazingly low mortality rate, and played a leading part in adopting inexperienced forward medical installations into efficient organizations for caring for the most severely wounded. During the bombings and shellings on the Anzio Beachhead, he displayed zeal and fortitude that inspired his associates and reflected great credit upon himself and the Medical Corps of the Army of the United States. He entered service from Roanoke, Virginia.

Official Seal
Mediterranean Theater of Operations

operate only on the Americans, and the Brazilians do most of the Italians and Germans besides the Brazilians, so are a great help. The Brazilian casualties have been very light so far. The Tenth Mountain Division is certainly paying for its assault on Mount Belvidere.

March 4, 1945—Valdiburo, Italy, Thirty-second Field Hospital

We are still very busy, and everyone is beginning to feel the strain a bit. This platoon of the Thirty-second Field Hospital is not what one would call a superior unit. Their mess is positively atrocious, and the sad part of the whole situation is that they don't realize it at all. I really chewed out Arkie Boyer, the captain who is in command of this unit, because the patients were not getting proper diets. Also, these teams that are working on twelve-hour shifts require some sort of relaxation and pleasure in food, which is the only source of pleasure during such a period. I do hope that Arkie gets things straightened out. *Arkie Boyer was, after the war, voted commander of the American Legion.* He seemed rather subdued after my chewing him out. We have moved around to so many various outfits that we know what can be done with army food, which with a little trouble and added effort can be quite palatable and adequate in every respect. But every so often the commanding officers, like the one of this platoon, let their cooks get by with just warming up some canned stuff and dumping it out, and that is all they do. It would appear that I think of nothing but my stomach, but that is not true. However, when the meals are the only recreation and break during the day, it is a bit disappointing to have them turn out to be such dismal flops. Henry Hoffman says that he has asked everyone how this outfit makes its coffee. It is really very fine coffee when we make it in our tent at night in a sort of old bucket. (It is simply great.) We do not understand how they can ruin it so thoroughly and completely in the mess. When Henry finds out their formula, he is going to make a careful record of it and so when he gets back to the States, he is going to serve it to all those people he doesn't like.

March 5, 1945—Valdiburo, Italy, Thirty-second Field Hospital

I got three fine boxes of food today. The green tomato relish came in great style, and I opened it immediately, spread some on bread, and ate a great deal. Unfortunately, the table in our tent sloped quite markedly and somehow the jar slid off the table and broke, so we scraped it up and transferred it to intravenous jars, from which it tasted just as good as ever, which is very good indeed.

March 8, 1945—Thirty-second Field Hospital, Valdiburo, Italy

Well, the Tenth Mountain Division has pushed the Germans off Mount Belvidere and is consolidating its position. Things have slowed down a great deal in the past day or two. Thor Torgelson, our most famous Olympic ski jumper and a member of the Tenth Mountain Division, was killed by a stray shell.

March 9, 1945—Valdiburo, Thirty-second Field Hospital

This weather is so nice and springlike that it doesn't seem like Italy at all. We had nothing to do this afternoon, so Phil Giddings, Colonel Simioni, who is a consultant studying shock care, and I took a three-hour walk up a mountain to this little village that is perched high in the mountains and if I ever saw a fairy tale town, this is it. The only access to the village is a dead-end cart path, and so there is no internal combustion engine traffic at all. The village doesn't occupy a space more than 100 yards long and 50 yards wide, but still has a very nice church, through which we were shown by the housekeeper of the local padre.

March 13, 1945—Valdiburo, Thirty-second Field Hospital

Charlie Rife and I took another long walk up a mountain to a village today for exercise and saw how these people do things as they have done them for centuries. An eighty-two–year–old woman was making wool threads. She had a handful of wool as trimmed from the sheep. She would tease out this wool, then give sort of a pear-shaped spindle a spin, and there you have another eight inches of thread. Life in these villages has to be seen to be believed.

March 18, 1945—Thirty-second Field Hospital, Valdiburo

We are having practically no work now, only a very occasional case scattered out among eight surgical teams. We still like to walk about the mountains, being careful to stay on the traveled paths to avoid any possible mines. When I take these walks, I always carry a pocketful of hard candy, which is available in all rations, but which no one ever eats. I give it to the kids, especially the cute little bashful ones that have not come in contact with many troops. I try my Italian by asking them how they are, what their names are, how old they are, and do they want some *caramelli*? They always say, "Grazia," very nicely. Then I take out pictures of my kids and say, "Mia Bambino," to which they always say "Bello" or "Bellissima." Quite a racket I have, but we both enjoy it.

March 20, 1945—Valdiburo

Three teams were pulled back today, namely George Stephenson, Phil Giddings, and Charlie Rife. I surely hate to lose my tentmates of Charlie Rife and his team. I don't like living alone so I moved up into a house where Larry Shefts and his teams are holed up. They will make good company for me.

March 21, 1945

This afternoon Reeve Betts, Larry Shefts, and I went back to a general hospital in Florence for a chest conference. Tom Burford is running this chest center at this hospital and is doing a very fine job of it. I really feel a little embarrassed by the way the Second Aux. people monopolize this business; they have had so darn much more big thoracic and thoraco-abdominal surgery that the other people really don't have too much to say. Charlie Rife was at the meeting, and he said he sure wished he was back up with us. Charlie really understands our problems and the workings of a field hospital, which relatively few people do. For example, one of the chiefs of surgery at a general hospital wanted to know why we didn't do secondary closures in four or five days, never once realizing that, about this period, our greatest concern for most of the patients is whether they will live or die.

March 23, 1945

Tonight we went to see a movie entitled *The Keys to the Kingdom,* but the sound was so terrible and the film kept jumping the track so consistently that we only stayed part of one reel. The setting was actually like a Hollywood version of movies near the front. There was a big shell hole in one wall of the building, no windows, and guys sitting on their helmets instead of comfortable chairs.

March 26, 1945—Headquarters, Florence

Colonel Forsee called me back to Headquarters this afternoon to talk about the records. He seems to be in a hurry to get this record business finished and has assigned everyone here at Headquarters to help with it. Since I am in charge, I gather that he means for me to crack the whip. Today we went down to see the Mediterranean basketball finals. The game was excellent, and you never heard such yelling in your life. These GIs are enthusiastic, all right.

March 28, 1945—Headquarters, Florence

The army has taken over a country club and golf course near our headquarters. Clubs and golf shoes are supplied by the army, but as far as balls are concerned "niente." I am writing home for my wife to send me two or three golf balls by first-class mail and maybe another dozen by regular mail.

April 1, 1945—Headquarters, Florence

Easter Sunday has rolled around and the third Easter I have been away from home. I remember going to Easter services in Rabat two years ago. The services were held in a racetrack grandstand, and I spent the whole time sitting there, far from home, watching a couple of storks wander around the racetrack infield feeding. At church this morning, the thought entered my mind that this is the real army now. Back in Africa it was, in retrospect, frightfully green and ignorant. This afternoon, Glen Gummess and I went out to this fine golf course to see if we could play some golf. Since no balls were available, we rented some tennis rackets and balls and had a couple of very snappy sets until Glen developed a blister on his thumb and one on his heel, which ended our activities. The clubhouse is lovely, and we sat on the terrace overlooking the valleys and mountains for almost three hours, just talking and enjoying it.

April 3, 1945—Headquarters, Florence

Colonel Forsee asked me to go to the Twenty-first General Hospital for a chest meeting, which I did. This war has certainly broadened my acquaintances very markedly. I have met so many good men and gotten to know them very well indeed. I never realized it until I got to this meeting, where I was greeted as if I were in a reception line. After all, we have been in this war, at least in this theater, for about two and a half years, so it is natural that I have a wide acquaintance.

April 11, 1945—Valdiburo, Italy

Back in the field again, with a big push eminent. You can see it and feel it everywhere. Henry Hoffman, Reeve Betts, and Larry Shefts are here with me—a nice bunch. Two evacuation hospitals and one general hospital team are supposed to join us. The improvement in this Thirty-second Field Hospital has been microscopic, if any. I am acting as surgical chief again. Scotty, poor guy, looks distinctly unhappy since my team has been disbanded.

April 12, 1945—Thirty-second Field Hospital, Valdiburo, Italy

We have settled down again in our mansion. Henry Hoffman, Larry Shefts, John McDaniel, and a new surgeon who has just joined our group, a boy by the name of Knowles Lawrence, together with myself are all neatly and cozily tucked into one not-too-large room with a radio, stove, clothes, boxes, Val packs, and various other items. It would drive a good housekeeper into a frenzy, but, most fortunately none of us is a good housekeeper. Maj. Pel Glazier with his team from the 170th Evac turned up today, and so did Colonel Forsee.

April 14, 1945—Valdiburo, Italy
The big jump-off occurred at 9:30 this morning. By 2:00 P.M., the casualties started to pour in, and we are absolutely swamped by 5:00 P.M. All four teams were working. Henry Hoffman, Reeve Betts, and I worked until 5:00 A.M., Larry and Glazier until 9:00 A.M. Fortunately, the Fifteenth Evac opened up at 6:00 P.M. tonight and took everything from then on. We even sent four patients from here forward to the Fifteenth Evac, which is set up two miles ahead of us. General Martin, Howard Snyder, and Lieutenant Colonel Bennett were around a couple of times today observing, but I was forced to ignore them more or less, since I was so busy.

April 15, 1945—Fifteen Evac Hospital, one mile north of Poretta
We slept until noon; then Henry Hoffman, Reeve Betts, and I moved up here together with Gardner, our shock man. They are really busy, having three or four general hospital teams working, too. The Tenth Mountain boys are running into trouble but are still advancing. Colonel Forsee came up at noon and brought our distinguished unit citation and insignia. It looks like we are members of a band with all these stripes on our left sleeves, but the colonel was sure tickled about this citation. The chief of surgery here is Charlie Wasden from Macon, Georgia, a swell gent. He volunteered to work the night shift and I was to work the day shift. I consider this very thoughtful of him.

April 16, 1945—Fifteenth Evac Hospital, Poretta
It was a hard day. Not a moment's rest, but we still got them pretty cleared up. Last night, a terrific barrage occurred over east of us on Highway 65. Must have been the Eighty-fifth, Eighty-eighth, Ninety-first, and Thirty-fourth Divisions jumping off. The Tenth Mountain boys are really moving ahead, from what we hear. The First Armored is also doing well pushing to the Po Valley, east of the Tenth Mountain. The Brazilians seem to be more or less pinched out and are having very few casualties. The job of chief of surgical services really keeps one moving about for twelve hours or so straight. The massive detail and small decisions to attend to are very trying! Of course, these evac hospitals don't keep busy for very long stretches, maybe a week or two;

156

then things ease up a great deal. On the other hand, our teams are of such a nature that we are constantly being sent to the busiest spots, so we don't get too much relief. It looks as if we will be moving forward, judging from the reports obtained from the wounded boys.

April 18, 1945—C Platoon, Thirty-second Field Hospital, Vergato, Italy

We worked rather steadily all day, and about 5:00 P.M. Colonel Forsee came up with instructions to move up to this platoon which is about twelve miles north of the Fifteenth Evac. We passed the Eighty-eighth, Forty-seventh, and Tenth Mountain Division clearing stations and moved up right next to a battery of Long Toms. We arrived just in time to get straightened out before dark. Just at twilight a Jerry plane that sounded like one of our Piper Cubs came over low and bombed and strafed in Vergato, about four blocks away. No damage to amount to anything.

April 19, 1945—B Platoon, Thirty-second Field Hospital, Lama, Italy, twelve miles southwest of Bologna on Highway #64

We have moved up again to this platoon this morning and gotten settled. We have been busy, but somehow when things are going well at the front, it doesn't fatigue and irritate one so much. The weather has been absolutely wonderful for the past few months. We were really swamped last night. I worked until 4:00 A.M. and slept until 7:30 A.M. Frank Hall arrived late last night with his team. The casualties are mostly Tenth Mountain and First Armored Division boys. They are pushing ahead at a great rate.

Due to the fact that at least half of our teams are in France, it has been necessary to supplement our surgical teams with teams from base hospitals. These new teams have some very fine surgeons in them, many from teaching institutions, but the difference in the manner in which our teams get the work done up here as compared to their work is pretty striking. This morning, I assigned this team, headed by an assistant professor of surgery of one of the large universities in the States, to do a case that involved a segment of the femoral artery in the right femoral triangle. He decided to use his knowledge and experiences in vascular surgery and attempted to do a vein graft. Well, we have neither the equipment nor the drugs for this type of vascular surgery. He kept removing veins, implanting them, and finding that they either coagulated so badly he couldn't use them or else the suture lines leaked excessively. In the meantime, casualties were piling into the admission tent and we had at least six belly wounds and a number of chest wounds, traumatic amputations from mines, et cetera, lying in

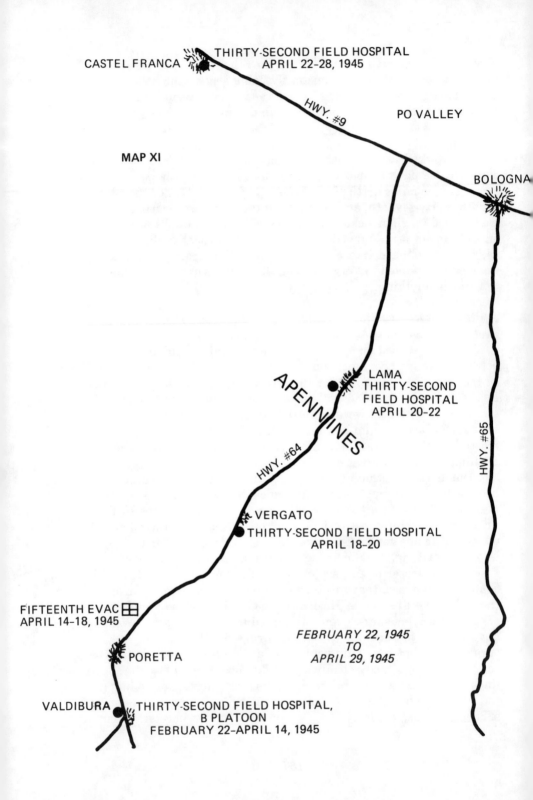

CASTEL FRANCA

THIRTY-SECOND FIELD HOSPITAL
APRIL 22-28, 1945

HWY. #9

PO VALLEY

MAP XI

BOLOGNA

APENNINES

LAMA
THIRTY-SECOND
FIELD HOSPITAL
APRIL 20-22

HWY. #64

HWY. #65

VERGATO
THIRTY-SECOND FIELD HOSPITAL
APRIL 18-20

FIFTEENTH EVAC
APRIL 14-18, 1945

FEBRUARY 22, 1945
TO
APRIL 29, 1945

PORETTA

VALDIBURA

THIRTY-SECOND FIELD HOSPITAL,
B PLATOON
FEBRUARY 22-APRIL 14, 1945

the shock tent. All these boys were in desperate need of attention, life-saving at that. Finally, after about three hours of this professor of surgery fooling around with the vein transplant, I had to order him to go ahead and ligate the artery, since it was so imperative that we get to the abdominal cases in the shortest possible time. Theoretically, he was doing the proper thing, but from a practical standpoint, with a mass of serious wounds backing up from his prolonged, more or less experimental surgery in the field, it was obviously not the place or time to attempt this type of surgery. He seemed to take my order in good grace and went ahead and did a couple of abdominal cases. After all, there is always a good chance that the kid whose artery was shot out will not have to have an amputation anyhow.

Two general hospital teams are with us. Stephenson and Phifer from the Thirty-seventh General, Shefts, and Hoffman are the other teams. We are in a nice meadow along the Reno River, with the Eighty-eighth Division Clearing Station. This was just taken yesterday afternoon, but the boys are moving so fast there is no cause for alarm. Truckload after truckload of prisoners are passing by going to the rear.

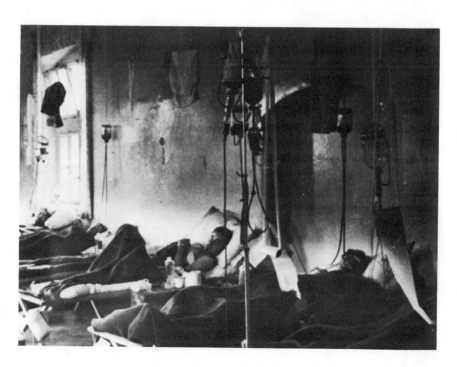

Intensive Care ward, Thirty-second Field Hospital, Valdibura, April 1945.

April 20, 1945—Thirty-second Field Hospital, Lama, Italy

We had only one patient to operate on during the past twenty-four hours. No one seems to know where anything is, including this hospital. We saw all our friends from the Eighty-eighth Division Clearing Station and had a nice volleyball game with them and then went over and drank some Yocky-Docky with them, reminiscing on previous times, particularly those of Pecchioli last summer.

Chapter V
Po Valley

I wrote in my diary this day, "Finally in the Po Valley! It sure is nice to look ahead——" I wrote the two brief sentences above, one of which was unfinished. That is the last word I have ever written in a diary. Now, some thirty years later, I have gone over the letters I sent home and recall some of the events. We broke out into the Po Valley to Highway 9, west of Bologna, and traveled west to a small town named Castelfranco Emilia. We immediately started setting up in a school or some such building assigned the improbable name of "Casa della Madre e del Bambino e Opera Assistenziale." As I recall, while they were setting up the operating room, I sat on a porch and wrote a letter home and started to write in my diary when all of a sudden shells started crashing about a block or two down the road. The Germans were still shelling Highway 9. This interrupted my diary, and I never did get back to it. The following entries to the end of the book are approximations of what I might have written.

April 22, 1945—Thirty-second Field Hospital, Castelfranco, Italy

It sure is nice to look ahead and to the right and left everywhere except the mountains behind us, without seeing a single mountain, hill, or such geographic obstacle that we have to take before we move. This is the first time in twenty months that such a situation has occurred. This country is beautiful, flat as a table, green, and very fertile and prosperous-looking. Of course, this being the Po Valley, we are the first and only hospital unit in this area. We have been, more or less (mostly more than less) working constantly. I have never seen anything like it before—truckload after truckload of German POWs streaming by constantly and large groups of prisoners marching rearward. The Germans moved out so fast there are numerous dead Germans scattered along the highway, which one has seldom seen in the past. Apparently, they were in such a hurry to get out that they had no time to remove their dead or wounded.

April 23, 1945—Castelfranco, Italy

We are working constantly, day and night, and our present teams are becoming thoroughly exhausted. We are the only hospital in the

Castelfranco Emilia—Casa della Madre e del Bambino e Opera Assistenziale.

Po Valley so far, and we are acting as collecting station, clearing station, and evac hospital as well as field hospital. It has really been a madhouse. We put in a call for four more teams to be sent up immediately to relieve our worn-out surgical teams.

April 24, 1945—Castelfranco, Italy

The teams we sent for yesterday fortunately arrived yesterday afternoon and were put immediately to work and worked all night. Since I am in charge of triage and also in making decisions about whom should be operated upon and who can wait, I have been forced to adopt a policy of preferential treatment: (1) the American soldier comes first, (2) Italian civilians come second, and (3) German POWs third. Actually there have been more POWs wounded than anyone else. There is one incident that has hurt my conscience a bit and made me wonder if I was doing the right thing in arranging for this order of preference of operation. We had this young, very handsome German top sergeant who had been shot through the buttocks and rectum. He was brought in in quite good condition, and I thought he could wait until we had finished our American boys. However, his condition deteriorated rapidly and there was still no place I could readily put him in for operation. Apparently, he had some sort of anaerobic infection, because his condition worsened rapidly, he became quite disoriented mentally, and at one time, he broke loose from his restraints and dashed out into

162

the hospital yard totally naked. It took about six of our boys to get him back in the hospital. His condition went down rapidly thereafter, and he died about twelve hours after admission. I'm fairly certain that had we not been so rushed with the American wounded, an early operation would have undoubtedly saved this man, but such are the fortunes of war.

This afternoon, things have begun to slow down since some of the evacuation hospitals have moved up ahead of us and there is practically nothing to do professionally. Believe me, we are ready for a good rest and I welcome doing nothing much.

April 27, 1945—Castelfranco, Italy

The war is moving so fast in this part of the world that we are really base section now. Even our headquarters has jumped us and is now in Modina, about ten miles up Highway 9 towards Milan. This is an unheard of and unprecedented situation.

Saturday, April 28, 1945

We have moved up Highway 9 toward Milan about fifty miles to a place called Piacenza. It appears that there will be little to do. This whole business is more like a race than a fight, and the whole Italian campaign seems to be more or less winding down in a rout. Naturally, we are pretty pleased about this. The thousands of prisoners streaming back are a beautiful sight even though they are frightfully dirty and unkempt.

April 29, 1945—Parma, Italy

A German hospital with about 200 patients was discovered some twenty miles back in a town called Parma, so we folded up again and moved back to take it over today. Krauts have one wing, and with us moving in, it has been a scene of utter confusion. To add spice to the affair, this city is a hotbed of partisans, and we are right next to their headquarters. They have all sorts of German small arms, and the rattle of machine guns, burp guns, rifles and pistols is heard at all times. I don't think they are shooting at anyone in particular, just shooting. Some of these partisans are pretty tough-looking characters, hair down to their shoulders, mostly pieces of German uniforms, all with a couple of revolvers, a submachine gun, a beltful of hand grenades and potato mashers, and about six bandoliers of ammunition strung about their anatomy. They did good work here in Northern Italy; even our own infantry admits that. I got a swell P-38, a German revolver, from one of them. It is a nice souvenir, and I got it for practically nothing. The natives are most friendly, and as we are absolutely the only Americans around, they act as if we were some sort of supernatural beings. Of course, one of the infantry divisions raced through here, but the people didn't come out during that time. The infantry was long gone when they did emerge. The main axis of advance is presently to the east and, of course, to the north, so that there is not even any traffic through here.

It sure feels queer to be walking around with a lot of Germans in the same building. They know they have been licked so they don't cause any trouble but jump to do anything you ask them to do. Their officers are very polite and correct, and some of them speak pretty fair English. All professional care of the patients, who are all Germans, is done by their own medical officers.

May 1, 1945—Parma, Italy

This is quite a town, and we are having a lot of fun in it. We spend our time sightseeing, shopping, and loafing. Parma is a town that is quite untouched by the war and unspoiled. The shops are very nice and have well-stocked, well-filled shelves. Bakeries are running full

First bridge across, the Po between Cremona and Lake Guarda—Tenth Mountain Division Advance, May 1, 1945.

164

tilt and have plenty of white flour. These conditions are quite unique; in no other part of Italy have I seen such things. This looks like about the best farming land I have ever seen and is all cultivated along very standard lines, so much so that it is a bit monotonous to ride any distance. The land is absolutely flat, with drainage canals through the fields. On a clear day, the snow-covered Alps are clearly seen in the north, and the Apennines, also snow-covered, to the south. Some nice jewelry stores are here that have some good filigree work and at a very reasonable price. I bought various knickknacks of this type to send to my wife. A pendant, which the man claims contains a real amethyst, was also bought. It is quite a large stone. I paid fifteen dollars for it and hope it is genuine. Parma is the city in which Verdi, the composer, was born. It is also the area from which Parmesan cheese comes. Believe it or not, we asked all over for Parmesan cheese, but there was none to be had. Probably it had all been shipped to Germany. Tonight, May 1, we got orders to come back to Headquarters to leave on assignment with a new field hospital. These moves on the spur of the moment are our specialty. It only takes about half an hour to get going. So we got packed and went.

May 2, 1945—East shore of Lake Guarda, Italy
The war in Italy is over! Thank the Lord! Praise be! Hallelujah! It all seems incredible to everyone, but it must be true. We didn't know about it until the 6:00 P.M. broadcast from BBC and then didn't believe it until we heard it repeated several times on subsequent broadcasts. Hostilities were formally ended at 12:00 noon, but no one around here knew anything about it until the 6:00 P.M. broadcast. I am sure that we all are deeply thankful and relieved. It is as if a great pressure has been released. After the 6:00 P.M. broadcast, some of the boys around here shot off several rounds from rifles and machine guns, but almost everyone felt that if they never heard another loud explosion it would just suit them fine. By 9:00 P.M., there was definitely no sign of a war. The artillery has been entirely quiescent, and nothing else whatsoever is going on. The end of the war is wonderful at this particular time. We got out of the damnedest mountains, the Apennines, about ten days ago, and here today we find ourselves right back in the mountains again, only this time they are really mountains. The Dolomite Alps stretch forbiddingly ahead; they are much more rugged and higher than the Apennines, and I just dreaded the thought of having to push through them another fifty miles or so. My feelings, of course, were nothing when compared to the feelings of the poor infantry. The Tenth Mountain Division had pushed ahead on both sides of Lake Guarda to the head of the lake. We are set up about halfway up the east side of

165

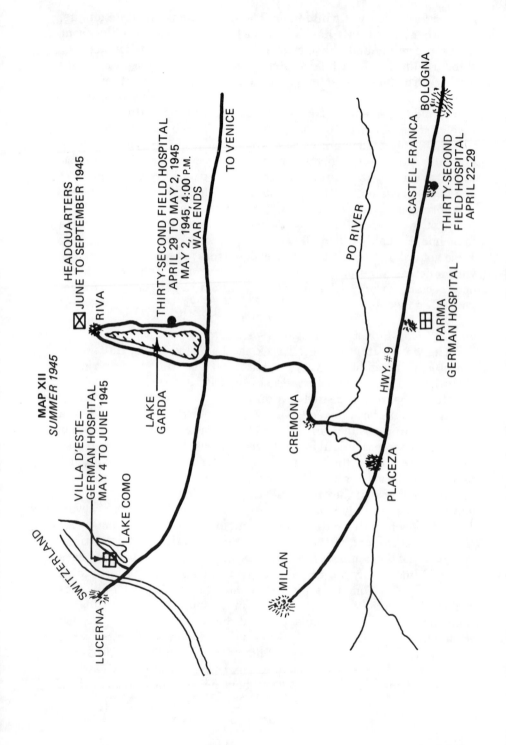

MAP XII
SUMMER 1945

VILLA D'ESTE—
GERMAN HOSPITAL
MAY 4 TO JUNE 1945

LAKE COMO

SWITZERLAND

LUCERNA

MILAN

HEADQUARTERS
JUNE TO SEPTEMBER 1945

RIVA

LAKE GARDA

THIRTY-SECOND FIELD HOSPITAL
APRIL 29 TO MAY 2, 1945
MAY 2, 1945, 4:00 P.M.
WAR ENDS

TO VENICE

CREMONA

PO RIVER

HWY. #9

PLACEZA

PARMA
GERMAN HOSPITAL

CASTEL FRANCA

BOLOGNA

THIRTY-SECOND
FIELD HOSPITAL
APRIL 22-29

the lake, but no patients have come to us because, I understand, the road on both sides of the lake is completely blocked with rockslides and blown tunnels, and transportation has of necessity been by boat to the Eighth Evac Hospital, which has moved up to the foot of the lake.

We had quite a trip today, leaving Headquarters early this morning. It was all very indefinite as to where we were going and what we were to do. We rode a good part of the morning and afternoon, finally ending up here at one of the Tenth Mountain Division clearing stations. We about froze driving up, running into a short but intense blasting snow-and-sleet storm. In our summer uniforms, it was bitterly cold. We stopped and took over a villa on Lake Guarda. Lake Guarda is an absolutely clear beautiful lake, with snow-covered Alps towering up thousands of feet all around it except the southern end. The Krauts had apparently used this villa we are in because there were straw pallets scattered around the floors. We swept these out and installed ourselves in some comfort, although we have no mess arrangements and are eating K rations again.

Villa on east side of Lake Guarda where we were set up at war's end, on May 2, 1945, 4:00 P.M., Thirty-second Field Hospital.

167

Chapter VI
Post-Hostilities

May 3, 1945—Modena, Italy

Since the war ended yesterday at noon, we don't seem to have any function up here on Lake Guarda. I tried to find out from Division and otherwise what we were supposed to do, and no one seemed to have the slightest idea. So I decided that since the war was ended and there was no reason for us staying here, we packed up and came back the 100 miles or so to Headquarters at Modena. Before we left Lake Guarda this morning, we heard that Col. William Darby, who was presently assistant commander of the Tenth Mountain Division, stepped out of his headquarters at a small hotel about five miles up the lake from us and was instantly killed when a shell landed right in his group. Colonel Darby was, of course, the man who put together the Rangers, had such a disastrous defeat at Cisterna, Italy, on the Anzio beachhead.

May 7, 1945—Modena, Italy

I was supposed to go up to take over the care of a captured German hospital today, but had to wait until Jim Mason, who is going to another hospital in the vicinity, was ready. We are going to Lake Como and Bergamo respectively. Many teams have come back into Headquarters, and pretty soon most of them will be back, I guess. I can't think of a more useless organization than ours at the present.

May 8, 1945—Villa D'Este, Lake Como

Jim Mason and I drove a weapons carrier almost all day, we let Jim off at Bergamo and finally arrived here at one of the showplaces of Italy, viz., the Villa D'Este, which is on Lake Como. There are no Americans around; in fact, the only ones I have seen in the entire district are two lieutenants of the Medical Corps and fifteen enlisted men who are here with me to run the administrative end of the hospital. The Germans are very polite and correct, with clicking heels and all.

We've heard on the BBC that war is officially over in Europe. As we arrived here, there developed a great clanging of bells and firing of machine guns, rifles, pistols, machine pistols, flares, and artillery pieces until one began to think that the war had just begun. The Italian partisans were celebrating the AP flash about the surrender in Europe. The Germans here are in a great state of alarm, fearing the Italian partisans will start shooting at the hospital. I got hold of an interpreter and went looking for the partisan chief and the mayor of this little town. I located the partisan chief and put on a vast show of bluff. With this show of authority and a very stern manner, I told him that the hospital was now a military hospital of the United States Army and that I would not tolerate a disturbance or shooting in or near the hospital and that I would hold him personally responsible to see that it didn't happen. He seemed properly impressed, and it wasn't long before things all quieted down in the vicinity, and it remained so all night. The hospital is called Luftwaffen Lazerette No. 1107. It is located on the west shore of Lake Como, in beautiful and spectacular surroundings. This resort facility was taken over by the Germans in January of 1944 and has been used for a center for orthopedics, maxillofacial, ENT, and medical cases. The Germans had built a new building for operating. The grounds are lovely, and there is a large park, an officers' club, tennis courts, a boat house, sail- and motor-boats, and just about everything one could ask for. I get sore as the devil when I think of all the miserable months we have spent in front of Cassino and in the Apennines while these bastards were living in the height of luxury in a place like this. Oh well, there will be some changes made now, I suspect.

May 10, 1945—Lake Como, Italy

Am getting pretty excited about the possibility of being home soon, and the sooner the better. My wife gave me stern instructions not to fly home. I informed her that I will ignore her admonitions completely and come home on the very first conveyance that will take me, be it airplane, rowboat, LST, liner, or submarine. Headquarters is still way back in Modena, which is about 150 miles from here, and we are really off the beaten track, so I expect I will be without mail for quite some time. This place is truly a wonderful spot—luxurious, in fact. I live alone in a villa on the lakeshore, the same house in which the major who commanded the hospital formerly lived. I, of course, have a fine room, a private balcony, a private bath, and three servants at my beck and call, and everything, is in fact, just like a resort hotel, which it is, of course. I make rounds of all the wards every morning, checking up on everything generally. The German staff doctors are required to be present at all these rounds. These two American lieutenants from a collecting company run the administrative end of the business, draw

Top dog with my private villa, shown here, Villa d'Este, Lake Como, May 1945.

rations, see about the guard, and what not. There is very little for me
to do. The German doctors are quite good, but I'm glad our boys were
treated in an American hospital most of the time. Many of our methods
and procedures are far superior to the Germans' methods. I am quite
amazed at the amount of infected wounds that one sees in this hospital,
and, in fact, I don't recall seeing uninfected wounds. Aseptic technique
to prevent the spread of infection is rather atrocious and largely ignored. The German officers gave a formal dinner for us three American
officers in their snazzy officers' club. They had elaborate floral decora-
tions, wine, liquor, champagne, and, incidentally, very fine food. It was
a very interesting evening because we found out all about the other
side's reactions to a lot of things. They seem to be entirely honest in
their remarks to us. They dread the future, and rightly so, because
they are still living here in a very fancy and unreal environment.

May 12, 1945—Villa D'Este, Lake Como, Italy
    This afternoon we took a trip about ten miles up the lake in our
private launch to see some famous azalea gardens, a truly magnificent

sight. We also stopped in the town where El Duce and his mistress, Clara, were caught while trying to escape to Switzerland. They were shot in this town and brought back to Milan and strung up by their heels in a public square.

May 14, 1945—Villa D'Este, Lake Como, Italy

I have been here a week and am almost entirely out of touch with the outside world, it seems. I had a radio installed in my suite, but rarely turn it on, even for the news. Somehow the news sounds awfully dull and trivial now that the war in Europe has ended and things are relatively static in the Pacific. All the excitement and tenseness of the past two and a half years was very unnatural and artificial, I know, but it will take a little time to become adjusted to the more prosaic type of news. This afternoon I came in from playing tennis and found Pat Imes, Paul Sanger, and Bill Pennington, all surgeons from the Thirty-eighth Evac, comfortably ensconced on my balcony with all the liquid fixings for enjoying themselves, the view, and the peaceful environment. The Thirty-eighth Evac is fully 100 miles from here, and how they knew I was here is surely a matter of conjecture. I had them stay over to dinner, which was good. They are still living in tents in a hot field and talked at great lengths about the breaks some people, namely me, get. I invited them to come up and stay a couple of days at our private country club, and I wouldn't be surprised if they did so.

I have my personal valet, a German, who was a valet to the German consul in Boston for a period of seven years before the war. Naturally, he is an expert in his line, although I think I shock him a bit with my informality at times. He, as do practically all the people, wishes to go to the United States after the war.

May 15, 1945—Villa D'Este, Lake Como

I have no inkling as to what might happen to me in the future. Black Robbie, our executive officer, was up today and didn't have a thing as far as rumors or plans. Headquarters is moving up to Lake Guarda, which will probably be the last move for them. Individuals are scattered from hell to breakfast all over Italy, most of the field hospitals acting as small station hospitals, with two or three teams attached to each platoon. I don't know what is going to happen to this hospital, since we are sort of off the beaten track and rarely see any visitors or officials. One of these days, though, I expect we will get word to get all cleared out and will have to return to Headquarters and work on the records, a thing I do not look forward to with any relish.

May 17, 1945

We are living pretty much like kings here, but somehow I don't seem to be enjoying it too much. We have wonderful food prepared by the professional chef at the Villa D'Este, and it is served very formally. Everyone bows, clicks heels, and all that stuff, which becomes a little monotonous after a while, and there is always the question of the sincerity of the people here, both Italian and Germany.

May 18, 1945

A good many cases of intramedullary pinning of fractured femurs are here in the hospital. Many are infected, but those that aren't seem to be doing extremely well. The Americans have no such device, and I believe the Germans are well ahead of us in this respect. Colonel Forsee asked me to write up a rather detailed report of these cases, which I did today and sent back to Headquarters.

There are certain enjoyable features connected with this place that do help. The civilian people around here are very effusive and shower me with invitations to tea, bridge parties, dinners, and dances, most of which I turn down. Part of the Italian nature is to try to get in the good graces of the people who are in power, regardless of principles and scruples, and then start asking for special privileges and favors. I suppose they have done this for centuries. The people around here have been very wealthy and lived in beautiful villas and are very polished socially. They apparently were not too antagonistic to the Fascists and Germans when they were in power. Hence one tends not to be bowled over by their enthusiastic attitudes toward Americans.

May 19, 1945—Lake Como, Italy

Jim Mason and Sam Driver came over from Bergamo this afternoon to take advantage of the luxuries of this place. They are spending the night and tomorrow with us and are suitably impressed with it all. Jim is very upset about being unlucky in cutting cards with me before we left Headquarters, to see who would go to Bergamo and who would go to Lake Como. I was lucky this time and drew Lake Como, and Jim had been very put out about the whole thing.

May 20, 1945—Lake Como, Italy

We suddenly got word last night that we were to evacuate one hundred patients today; consequently there was a lot of scurrying around getting ready the ones most suitable to travel. Word has leaked out that this will be a great place for a rest and recreation center for the army. I must admit it will be ideal for this purpose. I had written a rather lengthy report to the Fifth Army concerning this place. It seems that this evacuation is more or less the result of this report. The commanding officer of this German hospital is a German major, about thirty-five years old, who was a pilot as well as a doctor and flew his own plane. He crashed during the invasion of Crete about four years ago. He was severely burned about the face; as a consequence, he wears artificial ears, eyebrows, hair, and so forth. This gorgeous Greek girl who lives with him is credited with saving his life. He was going to commit suicide when he first caught sight of his face reflected in a windowpane. The girl told him she loved him and would stick with him, and so he changed his mind about suicide. They have one child. This gal has been with him for four years. I gather the Germans, like the the Italians, accept the carrying of mistresses with them as just a normal part of the baggage, at least for the officers. A collection of about a hundred and ten girls occupy a large villa about 100 feet down the lakeshore from my villa. These girls are restricted to their quarters, although they come out in various bikinis and lie in the sun and swim in the lake. We certainly have been very circumspect not to show any interest in these gals, who undoubtedly are camp followers, mistresses of various types, but all are from the rest of Europe rather than from Italy.

May 22, 1945—Lake Como, Italy

The tennis here has been one of my principal joys, and I have played practically every day. There is a very active tennis club in Como, which is about three miles from here. They have five excellent courts, and in addition to local players, there are a lot of players from Milan and other places that came to this region to escape the war.

Colonel Forsee came up this evening and is spending the night with us. He wants me to come back to Headquarters as soon as we can evacuate all the patients from this hospital, which will probably be sometime during the next week. As I anticipated, the records job is in the offing, which will keep me pretty well tied up, I imagine.

May 25, 1945—Lake Como, Italy

We are gradually getting this place cleaned out, only about fifty patients remaining, and if I can argue the German doctors into believing that some of the sick ones are transportable (which they are) I plan to have the last patient out in two more days. Headquarters is now over on Lake Guarda, which is where I was when the war in Italy ended. Lake Guarda is a beautiful lake, more so than Como, the mountains being much more rugged and awe-inspiring.

May 27, 1945—Lake Como, Italy

The last of our patients was shipped out this morning, although it took quite a little discussion to convince the German doctors that it was feasible to move a couple of them. I had so many good arguments on my side that there really wasn't much difficulty, and the German doctors soon came around to my way of thinking. I sent one of the German doctors in the ambulance containing the four sickest patients and was relieved to find that they made the trip to Milan, a distance of fifty miles or so, with no trouble whatsoever. So, I am out of a job and plan returning to Headquarters tomorrow.

May 29, 1945—Lake Guarda, Headquarters

Yesterday we made the trip from Lake Como to our headquarters here on Lake Guarda, a distance of about a hundred miles. With many deviations, we finally located the headquarters on the west shore of the southern part of Lake Guarda. No one had any idea where our headquarters was located. This is quite a nice place that Headquarters is in. A far cry from the days of Goat Hill, Bizerte, and other horrible places. We have all the advantages of a resort—not quite as good as Villa D'Este, but quite a nice place. When we came up to Lake Guarda on the last day of hostilities, the mountains looked very grim and forbidding, glimpsed through the swirling clouds and snow, but now everything is lovely and peaceful and green, not to mention quiet. The colonel lost no time in putting me to work. I started on these damn records the first thing this morning and will be busy with them indefinitely, I suppose.

June 2, 1945—Lake Guarda, Italy

There were a whole bunch of our officers here at Headquarters, and a lot of these were sent out today to these captured German hospitals to take charge of them. As a result, there are very few of us left here at the moment.

The water in Lake Guarda is marvelously clear and makes for fine swimming. One can see the bottom clearly in fifteen feet of water, and when diving from a springboard or diving tower, it is hard to estimate where the water really begins; one sees the bottom instead of the surface of the water. Every day numbers of fishing boats go out with nets to catch some sort of fish, I suppose they are very small fish, much like sardines. It is very picturesque to see these fishing boats going out. They have very high oar locks, and a row of four men stand up and face forward and all row in perfect unison.

June 6, 1945—Lake Guarda, Italy

Just when we thought we were all set for the summer in this very lovely place, we were informed today that we had to move. It seems that some of the senior officers have decided they want this place for rest and recreation center for bird colonel and general officers, so we are unceremoniously being kicked out. We will probably end up in tents in some dusty olive grove and will remain there the rest of the summer. It is all very discouraging. Jim Sullivan, our executive officer, who has been in command of the French-German detachment, drove in today from Augsburg, Germany, to give us a preliminary picture of the situation. It seems that this detachment is going to return to us in about a week to ten days, and there will be quite a migration inasmuch as about two-thirds of our teams are with this detachment.

June 8, 1945—Lake Guarda, Italy

It seems that we will be moving tomorrow, and I don't believe we will be any worse off than we are now. Fifth Army came to our rescue and gave us a nice resort hotel at the head of Lake Guarda in a resort town called Riva. They say it is pretty swell, so I am looking forward to seeing this place.

June 9, 1945—Riva, Italy

We came up the west side of Lake Guarda, passing through many tunnels that had been enlarged and contained a great deal of machinery that the Germans had installed to manufacture weapons of war. Of course, many of these tunnels had been blocked, but our engineers had cleared out a passage through them. We finally arrived at Riva and found a hotel that is called Grande Albergo Lido. It is about the swankiest spot on the lake, although old and sort of down-at-the-heel at present. The surroundings are superb. This hotel had been reserved by Corps Headquarters, but they were uncertain as to whether they would use it or not, so the army turned it over to the Second Aux. The Germans had been using the building as a hospital, so most of the furniture is gone, but there are plenty of beds, chairs and wardrobes. The lake is very deep here and very blue, with sheer mountains rising all around us that in certain lights seem to overhang the place. The sun goes behind these mountains about 4:30 P.M., so the evenings are cool and shady. I found a couple of tennis courts nearby this afternoon and have arranged to have them reserved for our group.

June 11, 1945—Riva, Italy

This record business is going ahead full blast. We have the whole bottom floor of quite a large accessory building, with about ten doctors, eight nurses, and five enlisted men working daily from 9:00 to 4:00. The colonel has made me editor-in-chief of this massive report, and it is my responsibility now to see that it all gets together in good shape. I'm not at all anxious to undertake this thing, but orders are orders, and I guess I'll have to do the best I can.

June 12, 1945—Riva, Italy
This was our eleventh wedding anniversary and an appropriate message sent home.

June 14, 1945—Riva, Italy
Tonight has been quite a welter of confusion, greetings, reminiscences, and introductions; the bunch from Germany rolled in about dark by truck convoy. Almost two-thirds of our teams had been attached to the Seventh Army, working through southern France and into Germany. It was great to see all of my old friends again, including Gordon Madding, Charlie Westerfield, Paul Kennedy, George Donaghy, and many others with whom I had worked and become very good friends. They had a lot of things to tell us about their campaigns and on the whole seemed to have had it much easier than we had it here in Italy. They claim that Bavaria and the Tyrol are the most beautiful places they have ever seen, for scenery, neatness, and cleaniness. A great many of the men had seen the concentration camp in Dachau and vouched for the authenticity of the reports that were published about the atrocities, the bodies piled up like cordwood, and the rest. The yarns and reminiscences were flying thick and heavy all evening, both from their end and ours. There is no question in their minds that Italy was the toughest campaign of all.

June 15, 1945—Riva, Italy
There has been such a state of confusion with the arrival of the southern France contingent that there was no use in trying to work again. I therefore wangled a car, got four buddies, and away we went to Milan, which I had seen only very briefly before. It is about a hundred miles from Milan, so we didn't get too much time there. The two principal things of interest were (1) the cathedral, which is quite magnificent, although I am getting a bit fed up with seeing cathedrals of any kind, and (2) Leonardo da Vinci's painting *The Last Supper*. This latter painting is on one end of the wall of a small chapel in a church called the Santa Maria dela Grazia. The paint was applied directly to plaster, and it is in an alarming state of disrepair and fading badly. It was well

that they had this particular wall well sandbagged, as a bomb or two had landed directly in the courtyard, knocking the roof entirely off the chapel and demolishing the two lateral walls, but leaving the wall with the painting intact. We did what other sightseeing we could, but found nothing of particular interest.

June 18, 1945—Riva, Italy

I seem to be getting into pretty good physical condition again, much to my surprise. We play tennis every evening after dinner, and my legs no longer get sore, stiff, or lame. Tonight, we even played five sets of doubles and I didn't feel a bit tired afterwards. The pressure is really on in regards to this records business. The colonel wants this report in by July 15, so the work goes on seven days a week, including nights. It is now 12:15 A.M., and I am just returning from working on the report. It is pretty obvious that I won't get to go home until this report is finished, so I am tackling the job with the utmost determination and energy.

June 25, 1945—Riva, Italy

Another one of our nurses got married this afternoon to an air-force officer. The ceremony took place on the front steps of the hotel and was quite impressive. There were bridesmaids, flower girls, and all the rest. It was really a very pretty wedding, outdoors, with the lake just in front of them and those tall mountains looming up as a backdrop. We had quite a party afterwards.

June 26, 1945—Riva, Italy

Colonel Forsee, when we first got to know him, was a complete teetotaller and frowned on any alcoholic activity whatsoever. He is the son of a Baptist minister and was apparently brought up very strictly. However, during the past two and a half years, we have gradually broken down his excessively strict upbringing, and even when he came out in the field, we would mix up some "Yocky-Docky" and he was more or less forced to join in the communal cup. When we took over this place, someone found a whole warehouse full of excellent vermouth and other drinks and had liberated an entire truckload and brought it over to our headquarters. It was not long before we were having an open bar before each dinner with plenty to drink. The Colonel even takes an occasional drink or so, wonder of wonders! We have also been getting ice sent up from some place that the engineers have taken over, so that our drinks are just wonderfully cold and delicious. Word has spread throughout the area that we have this cocktail hour every evening before dinner, and Gen. Joe Martin, Fifth army surgeon, appreciating our company more than the company he is thrown in with, other bird colonels and generals back at the southern end of the lake, almost routinely comes up for cocktail hour, dinner, and conversation afterwards. We show him really very little respect and treat him just like one of us. He was very upset and aggravated a night or two ago when he proposed that we should all volunteer to go to Japan. This proposal was met with laughter and jeers, much to his apparent disgust. It's about time that some of these Regular Army officers realize that there is something in life other than the army, and we surely let the general know it.

June 29, 1945—Riva, Italy

The most "popular" guy in this whole outfit is none other than yours truly. As officer in charge of professional services, I am constantly referred to as a "slave driver." The building in which we do our work is referred to as "the Dachau gas chamber," and I am accused of having worn out any number of rawhide bullwhips. It really is some job, one that no one desires at all, including myself. It seems quite certain that we will not be going to the Pacific, so that is something to be thankful for. Quite a number of our officers, maybe twelve or fifteen of our lowest-point men, have been transferred to hospitals that are known to be going to the Pacific, and if we were going as a group, I don't believe these transfers would have been made.

July 5, 1945—Riva, Italy

Well, we learned today that we probably won't get home until late in the fall. It is a very bitter dose to take, and one can feel the resentment sweeping the outfit. It does seem a shame to keep one hundred highly trained and skilled surgeons and anesthesiologists sitting over here doing nothing, with no possible chance of being needed. Surely, they are needed much more back home among the civilians. I understand there have been quite a few questions raised in Congress and elsewhere regarding the army keeping unneeded doctors unduly long.

July 9, 1945—Lake Guarda, Italy

I am keeping frightfully busy and working as hard as I can. We are getting together thirty-five hundred abdominal cases, which are my principal concern. I personally am writing up the gastric section, supervising and criticizing the write-ups of sections by twelve other men, and attending to many details. I am probably the laziest and the worst procrastinator of any man doing this work, so I have to grin to myself when I start prodding these other men to get this stuff in. I have an editorial board consisting of Phil Giddings, who knows about things like gerunds, substantive clauses, and similar mysterious rules of grammar. Sam Childs of Denver, who is a swell fellow and very intelligent, knows about things mathematical, such as logarithms, mathematical progressions, factors, et cetera. All these things are a complete mystery to me.

July 11, 1945—Riva, Italy

I may be an old man, but I have gotten in pretty good physical shape. This process has not been painless; quite the contrary, the moaning, groaning, limping, and shuffling mass of protoplasm seen limping about the place since war ended was I. There have been some results of this conditioning process, since I can play three hard sets of singles and pretty consistently beat these youngsters, ages twenty-eight to thirty-two, much to their disgust. They are free with their caustic comments about my age, appearance, and lack of speed, but I still manage to beat them quite frequently. Bill (Bow-Wow) Bowers, who is forty years old, is my doubles partner, and invariably we beat any combination that is thrown against us, which really burns up the youngsters. We really rub it in about the two old, decrepit white-haired gentlemen beating the pants off these boys.

July 16, 1945—Riva, Italy

We have been awarded additional battle stars, and I have six, also an inconspicuous Bronze Arrowhead to wear on the European-Mediterranean ribbon. This arrowhead was awarded for making the D day landing at Salerno. These mean additional points, but as far as I can tell, points mean nothing toward getting home early.

July 19, 1945—Riva, Italy

Colonel Forsee has returned from Caserta with some pretty hopeful news about our getting home before our previous estimated date of sailing. Congressmen back home are making quite an issue of the army keeping doctors longer than necessary when there is no possible need for them. We will get home within the next two or three months, infinitely better than twice that long.

It is really beginning to get hot now, but compared to other summers, I feel that this heat is very bearable indeed. We have ice this summer, which was never available in previous summers, and besides we have this fine, cool lake to get into when we feel the heat too much. Another good thing about this place is that invariably a cool, strong breeze starts up about noon and lasts until dark.

179

July 27, 1945

Phil Giddings, Sam Childs, and I have carefully edited each paper, suggesting corrections, additions, or deletions and even rewriting some of it. As there are twenty or so papers, running about twenty typewritten pages each, it has all been a terrific job. In addition, Phil, Sam, and I are supposed to write up a good part of the report ourselves. We are finding out some fairly interesting things and have worked out what we call a "multiplicity factor" in abdominal wounds to explain some very puzzling things. I really believe this will be the most comprehensive and important report on war casualties that has ever been turned in. Colonel Forsee places a very high importance on it, and it seems to me he realizes that this will be a notable work.

August 6, 1945—Riva, Italy

Today is unquestionably V day everywhere, but one would never guess it around here. The Japanese surrender was expected, but no one here got very excited about it. It seems anticlimatic to us, and there were no celebrations, public or private. We are all so burned up about being kept over here so long that the men were just not in the mood for celebration at all.

August 17, 1945—Riva, Italy

Colonel Churchill, our consulting surgeon, stopped in here at our headquarters for an overnight stay. He definitely said that the orders had been issued to send our group home and he was surprised that we hadn't received them.

August 21, 1945—Riva, Italy

It is reliably rumored that orders are in the process of being sent to us disbanding the Second Auxiliary Surgical Group and shipping the men home at an early date. As a consequence, everyone is getting pretty excited. Of course, these orders won't apply to me at once, but it will not be much longer.

August 26, 1945—Riva, Italy

The orders came through today for the group to go to Verona to catch planes for the embarkation point. There will be only about ten of us left after the main group leaves.

August 27, 1945—Riva, Italy

I got up at 4:30 A.M. to eat breakfast with all the guys who are going home today. They left about 5:30 A.M., going to Verona, to be flown from there to Naples. About seventy of them have gone and some fine fellows among them. I sure hated to see them go, especially Reeve Betts, Bill Bowers, Charlie Westerfield, Paul Kennedy, George Donaghy, Gordon Madding, and Trogh Adkins and a lot more that were my particular friends. I do hope I can keep in contact with a lot of them in the future.

August 31, 1945—Riva, Italy

We have gotten ahead of our typist somewhat, since we are making corrections. So Phil Giddings, Larry Shefts, and I took a little trip north of here in a borrowed jeep. We went up to Trento, Bolzano, and Merano, where George Hopkins is still running a German hospital. Hoppy took us up to this nice hotel, which was perched on top of a mountain; the only way up there is by cable car, which mode of conveyance is quite an experience in itself, and the first I have ever ridden. It was a very beautiful sight looking over the valley and the other mountain ranges from this spot. We are taking off tomorrow on the way home!

Our headquarters, Albergo Lido, situated in Riva at head of Lake Guarda. This is where we assembled the "Book"; *Forward Surgery of the Severely Wounded* in the summer of 1945.

181

September 7, 1945—Florence, Italy

We are quartered in the redeployment center in Florence, presumably getting checked over and processed for shipment home, but nothing has happened yet. I guess everything just takes time in the army.

September 8, 1945—Florence, Italy

I played golf today with Sam Childs at the Ugolino Golf Club, one of the seven golf clubs that are in existence in Italy. It isn't a very good course, but I enjoyed it thoroughly. This was the first time I had played golf in almost three years. I finally used some of the golf balls that were sent to me way back last winter. My score was 80, which wasn't bad, I thought, after all these years.

September 10, 1945—Florence, Italy

We are staying at the Anglo-American Hotel now. It is a very nice place, and the food is quite good. I called up Professor Valdoni today and had the Professor and Mrs. Valdoni down for dinner. I don't think they have been out in public places very much for a year or so, and they seemed very much to enjoy it.

September 11, 1945—Florence, Italy

The report is finally all nicely bound and ready to go in. It consists of two volumes of about 500 pages each. There are only seven copies, and Colonel Forsee presented me with a set of them with much ceremony and a nice inscription on the flyleaf. I thought this was very nice of him indeed, and I shall mail a copy home since it is too big to be lugging around. The Valdonis had Colonel Forsee, Sam Childs, Phil Giddings, and me out to their house for dinner tonight. It was very lovely. We took the books we had just had bound for the professor to look over. He did so very thoroughly and seemed very much impressed, insisting that they should be published at the first opportunity.

September 13, 1945—Florence, Italy

Well, that damned, incompetent, irresponsible jerk of an inspector general is supposed to return tonight from his vacation. He made all of us sit here twiddling our thumbs for an entire week.

September 14, 1945—Florence, Italy

The Second Auxiliary Surgical Group is no more. It was officially disbanded this morning, with no tears shed, since it was strictly a wartime organization. We are supposed to get orders tomorrow to report to a redeployment center at Pisa.

September 15, 1945—Rome, Italy

The second stage of our journey home has been taken. We left Florence late this morning and arrived here in Rome about 7:30 P.M. and are staying at the Excelsior Hotel again.

September 16, 1945—Caserta, Italy

We stayed overnight in Rome and drove on down here to Caserta this afternoon, reporting to the surgeon's office here.

September 18, 1945—Caserta, Italy

We are waiting for our orders to be issued, putting us aboard a plane or boat going to the United States, and it is dull waiting. This afternoon, Harvey Allen, Phil Giddings, and I drove up to Cassino and Monte-Cassino, going through the very familiar territory were we had such very rough times in the fall of 1943 and the winter of 1944. The devastation of war has been cleaned up to a remarkable degree in twenty months. We drove up to the abbey, which is still nothing but a mass of rubble, and could easily see how the Germans were not deterred in the least by its destruction. There were all sorts of caves, catacombs, and thick protective walls that afforded the Germans any protection they might need. Interestingly enough, there were still some German bodies along the ridges north of the abbey, or at least there were portions of bodies that were quite mummified. I don't know who is responsible for moving these gruesome remains, but here they are still, some twenty months after the place was taken.

September 19, 1945—Sorrento, Italy

Here we are again at the Grande Albergo Vittoria, across the bay from Naples, and it is a very lovely spot still. In fact, it is much nicer than it was when I was here in December of 1943. Of course, things have quieted down a lot and everything is more sedate and respectable. I played three sets of tennis this morning and went sailing in the bay with Phil Giddings this afternoon.

September 20, 1945—Sorrento, Italy

We got the good news this afternoon! Our orders are in to report to the redeployment center in Naples for shipment to the U.S.A., and from what we can gather from scuttlebutt, it is much like going to jail to get in one of these redeployment centers. It seems one goes there and waits for a week or ten days before anything really happens. One isn't allowed to leave execpt in the evenings, and even then there isn't really any place to go, Naples being what it is today.

September 22, 1945—Naples, Italy, Seventh Redeployment Center

There is absolutely nothing to do here, and it is all very monotonous and boring. It seems that they have made a special dispensation for medical officers, keeping them here just because of the possibility of needing someone on a Liberty ship that is taking a small detachment home. Other officers get to go in four to five days, but medical officers are kept here for ten days to two weeks. It seems that we are most likely to be put aboard a Liberty ship when we do get away, since the transports are all being sent mostly to the Pacific. Very few individuals get to fly home. "Points" mean nothing whatsoever toward getting one home. I think I have more points now than anyone in the whole theater. I have 156, while most of the men going home with me have around 80, but this means nothing. I figure I have about 115 days' terminal leave when I do get home, which will be of some help.

September 23, 1945—Naples, Italy

To relieve the boredom of this "Repple-Depple" (after only one day of it), Oscar Hampton and I decided to hitchhike up to Caserta for a good meal and to see our friends. This we did. Colonel Stanley, who is now theater surgeon, and Colonel Churchill invited us out to their place for a few drinks and to dinner in the big shots' mess—that is, one had to be a bird colonel or higher to eat in this mess regularly.

Colonel Churchill, who is truly a remarkable man, has about the keenest mind of anyone I have ever met and the ability to stimulate others to a very marked degree. We had a most interesting and enjoyable evening discussing all sorts of medical and surgical things, as well as discussing various men who had done good and bad work in the theater, as the case might be. I believe everyone would be surprised to know how much Colonel Churchill knows about the work of each medical officer, as well as their various limitations and abilities. Colonel Churchill had a chance to look over the abdominal section of our report and thought we had brought out quite a bit of material that had never been thought of before. He wants to get the whole report published as a reference book when he gets back to the States.

September 27, 1945—Naples, Italy

Tonight my name, along with those of about a hundred other officers, went up on the bulletin board "On Orders," which means that probably within forty-eight hours or so, we will be aboard some ship—what kind we don't know for sure. Since the only ships in the harbor are Liberty ships, it unquestionably will be a Liberty ship.

September 28, 1945—Naples, Italy

We made frequent trips to the bulletin board, looking for our definite orders to embark, but nothing yet. Colonel Forsee called up this afternoon to ask us to come up to Caserta for dinner and cocktails for a nurse whose rank is major and who is to be married in a few days. Transporation was sent for us. We enjoyed the party!

September 29, 1945

Approximately every two hours, I laboriously descend the four flights of stairs, stare at the bulletin board, and ascend the stairs dejectedly. Nothing whatsoever appears. I think one has to be of a very special type of mentality to get to like the army, a mentality characterized by complete patience and no frustrations or interest in the future except from an economic viewpoint. I don't seem to have these sterling characteristics and definitely do not like the army. This Repple-Depple is overflowing; it has a capacity of ten thousand, and at present there are approximately eighteen thousand people here trying to get to the United States.

September 30, 1945—Naples, Italy

The days simply crawl by and at an unbelievably snaillike pace. It seems more like three years since we left Riva rather than three weeks, and each day is a month long. Our names are still posted prominently on the alert board, but nothing whatsoever happens. Almost no ships are coming into Naples now and very few are leaving it, so it is very discouraging. Almost all of the Regular Army officers have long since skipped home, so that actually a bunch of civilians are running the occupation forces, which further irritates everyone.

October 2, 1945—Naples, Italy

Today is again my birthday, but no celebration whatever is in order.

This afternoon Phil Giddings and I went down to see Major Jackson, who is running this business. He is a nice youngster, and he explained in detail that we were supposed to be shipped on a Liberty ship called the *Alexander Hamilton* which had brought a load of flour over to Italy to feed the starving Italians. On September 27, the dockworkers struck because they thought the POWs who were also put to work unloading ships were taking bread from their mouths. He assured us the ship would be ready to sail on the fifth or sixth of October, and it was impossible to reschedule anyone. I guess we have to make the best of it, but are silently cursing the Italians, the army, and the war. We kept on waiting.

October 5, 1945—Naples, Italy

After weeks of frustration, hopes, mostly dashed, and cussing, we are finally going to board the good ship *Alexander Hamilton*, which is a Liberty ship, at 7:00 A.M. tomorrow, and tomorrow evening at this time, we ought to be out of sight and smell of Italy. Come to think of it, I am getting right much excited.

October 6, 1945, to November 8, 1945—Atlantic Ocean

We boarded the old relic of a Liberty ship called the *Alexander Hamilton* on October 6, 1945, and pulled out after several hours' delay, into the Mediterranean Sea. Majors and captains on board have above deck quarters. There are about 300 officers and about 300 enlisted men on the ship, all willing to undergo almost any hardship in order to get home. It soon became apparent that this old Liberty ship badly needed some repair work done, since there was a marked hiss with every turn of the propellers, as if the main gasket were leaking. We dashed along at approximately five or six miles an hour across the Mediterranean to the coast of North Africa, where we took on ballast consisting of iron ore. We then headed through the Straits of Gibraltar and got a nice look at this remarkable scene. All day the ship gradually crawled along, making no more than six miles an hour; it seems that the crew could do nothing to repair the leaking gasket or speed up the ship. About the mid-Atlantic, a severe storm hit us, which was somewhat disagreeable and frightening to some people, but I think the captain headed into the wind at top speed and managed to keep things together. After about three weeks of creeping along, we were confronted with an apple and a glass of reconstituted powdered milk for lunch one day. Supper was no better, so some of we senior officers held a committee meeting to know what was going on, since none of the crew would give us any answers. We therefore proceeded up to the captain's quarters and confronted him with the situation. We wanted to know what went, with no food. He said he only had three weeks' supply of food for the journey and since we had been on the sea for three weeks, we were out of food and would have to be on very short rations for the rest of the time, which he estimated to be approximately one more week. This did not make sense to us, and we were sure that something could be done about it. We officers were unwilling to accept this rather lame excuse, feeling that the United States would certainly have an ample supply of food for a delayed voyage, and even had we run out of food, a Catalina flying boat or a fast destroyer could come out to meet us and supply rations. In the meantime, one of the enlisted men had found out from one of the ship's crew that there was, indeed, a large food locker filled

Great Day! At last boarding that old relic of a Liberty ship, the S.S. *Alexander Hamilton* bound for home, Naples, Italy, October 1945.

with food. We called on the captain and demanded to be shown around the ship's food lockers and storage space. He sent a mate with us, and we noticed a door that the mate seemed to be avoiding. We demanded that he open it. Here, indeed, was a vast quantity of food, with a freezer containing frozen meats and other delicacies. These great merchant mariners, who were still drawing combat pay for overseas duty, had planned to use only the food in the other lockers, leaving this secret locker full, but reporting it as having been used up on the trip. Then, on the next run back to Italy, they would sell this food on the black market at a great profit to themselves. Apparently, one of the crew had felt that this was either not the right thing to do or he was not getting his share of the booty. He had told one of the enlisted men, who told us. Most of the officers that were passengers on this ship had been in combat and were tough, hardened cookies; some of these wanted to either kill the captain or lock him up in the brig until we got to the States. Undoubtedly, the ship's officers and crew sensed this, so we ate very well indeed the rest of the voyage, which was a week. We discussed at length what we were going to do to report this stinking, lousy bunch of merchant mariners when we got to the States and had plans all set to send a delegation to Washington for an immediate investigation. However, on the morning of November 8, 1945, we could see the low-lying shore of Cape Henry and the Chesapeake Bay entrance. We went into Hampton Roads and docked. I thought by this time the troops had been more or less forgotten, but there indeed was a military band playing and a large number of Red Cross workers and other people to welcome us. We were taken to an army post that afternoon, and that night we really had a wonderful meal served at the mess. I ate a whole head of lettuce and drank at least a gallon of sweet milk, the first I had had in over three years. Of course, the steaks and so forth were not turned down either. As soon as we were allowed off the post, I called my wife. Everything else, including the merchant marines, was completely and thoroughly dismissed from my mind as being inconsequential. I was home again!

Chapter VII
Retrospectus

Thirty-five years later, the war in Italy seems really ancient history, yet much of it seems quite lucid and vivid, particularly when the mind is prodded by reading something like my diary.

It seems likely that our experiences in forward military surgery were and will continue to be unique in military history. Not until World War II was the concept of treatment of the severely wounded far forward in mobile surgical hospitals carried out. It seems unlikely that surgical teams will operate in the division area in the future, as we did. Certainly, the development of the helicopter greatly speeded the transportation of casualties in the Korean and Viet Nam Wars, and it will probably be the mode of transporation of the wounded in the future wars. However, both the aforementioned wars did not result in the mass casualties encountered in World War II; therefore, there still may be need of forward mobile hospitals to handle mass casualties. Furthermore, weather conditions in Italy made flying impossible during much of the rainy season. Similar meteorological conditions in future wars might require the use of mobile surgical hospitals working far forward.

Although treatment of abdominal, thoracic, head, and extremity wounds has changed or improved little in the past thirty years, cardiovascular wounds were certainly poorly treated during World War II. Present-day techniques of vascular surgery undoubtedly will preserve many extremities, and some truncal or neck vascular injuries can be handled much more effectively than they were treated during World War II. Nevertheless, in the presence of mass severe casualties, the possible preservation of an extremity cannot take precedence over lifesaving surgery of the abdomen and chest.

The following comments, which are not guaranteed to be 100 percent correct or accurate, summarize some of my personal impressions and opinions about the Italian campaign.

Role of the Italian Campaign in World War II

One has the suspicion that our military leaders in Italy were poor students of history. From the days of Hannibal on through the various invasions of Italy by the French and Spaniards, active fighting only

189

occurred in the late spring, the summer, and the early fall. Winter fighting was impossible for them. Despite these lessons of history, the Allied command pushed active fighting throughout the fall and winter of 1943 and 1944, with disastrous results. Thousands of casualties resulted from this unproductive winter fighting. Despite the lesson that should have been learned from the winter of 1943–44, active fighting and offensive attacks were pursued regardless of the obvious dismal results in the winter fighting in the Apennines in 1944–45. Not until January of 1945 did the high command finally issue orders for the infantry to take up defensive positions, assuming a holding posture, except in isolated instances, until May of 1945.

Those who served in Italy will agree that the greatest understatement of all times was uttered by Winston Churchill when he termed this area "the soft underbelly of Europe." The terrain was a nightmare of one mountain after another, to be taken almost foot by foot. Possibly the only comparable misstatement is contained in the phrase "sunny Italy"; it rained torrents for about five months during the winter. Italy soon became a secondary front, with the invasion of France on June 6, 1944, and particularly with the invasion of southern France in August of 1944. In short, the Italian campaign did little except establish air bases for strategic bombing, but it did serve to keep a good many of the best German divisions engaged.

In the final analysis, the most valuable role of the Italian campaign was very accurately summed up by Dr. Edward D. Churchill, who wrote that "Italy was the experimental laboratory not only for surgery but also for medicine as a whole, for ordnance, for equipment, and, as many are reluctant to recall, even for rations. This theater was the proving ground for the greater task that was to come."

The Enemy

The German soldier was, in my opinion, generally the best in the world. He obeyed orders implicitly, never gave up without a stubborn and vicious fight, and showed amazing stamina and courage. The Germans were masters at taking every advantage of terrain and were artists at contriving interlocking, well-concealed defenses. Without air support, with very restricted artillery, and with largely animal-drawn transport, they fought the Allies practically to a standstill in Italy. The Germans were also masters of nasty warfare; booby traps and delayed action bombs were commonly used. Germans had large Teller land mines for blowing up tanks and vehicles, "Bouncing Betsy" antipersonnel mines, which, on being tripped, jumped out of the ground about three feet and exploded, scattering ball bearings over a wide area. But the nastiest mine of all was the German "Shu" mine, which was made of nonmetallic material and could only be found by probing. We first encountered this Shu mine in January of 1944 before Cassino, and from then on we encountered its results with great frequency. It blew off a great many feet and accounted for fully 90 percent of our reported 1,000 leg amputations. Of course, the German 88 became legendary for its accuracy and effectiveness as a multipurpose weapon. The German "Tiger" and "Panther" tanks were superior to any tanks that the Allies had. One reaction of the German soldier that greatly surprised me was the almost craven fear of the soldier when professionally encountering a physician. This fear almost amounted to terror. In trying to figure out this phenomenon, I finally concluded that it was the result of barracks tales of the cruelty and lack of regard for pain and suffering exhibited by the German doctors. In truth, this was partially true; many procedures were done without local or general anesthesia, where clearly such anesthesia was indicated.

Our Allies

The Fifth Army was really a polyglot outfit. There were the stoical, no-need-to-hurry-or-get-excited Britishers, the Americanlike South Africans, the French Foreign Legion, with their fierce and knife-wielding Berber "Goums" (Moroccans and Algerians), the Indian Ghurkas, excellent fighters, the Polish, with their hatred of the Germans, the Canadians, forming part of the Special Service Force, effective fighters, and the American-born Japanese Neisei of the 100d Battalion, out to prove their patriotism and bravery, which they did in a spectacular manner, the New Zealanders, much like the South Africans, and the Brazilians, who held a sector of the line effectively during the winter of 1944 and 1945. And finally, there were the Italians, a high-spirited division that failed dismally as fighters in their one attack on Mount Lungo. Thereafter, the Italians were used mostly as mule skinners and in service installations.

The Air Support

The air-force planes, both strategic and tactical were a pleasant and cheering sight for those of us looking up from the ground. They performed well in knocking down towns, disrupting airfields, and messing up marshaling yards. However, from the ground level, they did not seem to do much to deny the Germans supplies; nor did they injure the German soldier appreciably. The accuracy of their bombing left a good deal to be desired, as witnessed by the bombing of Venafro, with the production of many Allied and civilian casualties, when their target was Cassino, more than twenty miles away. Their bombing of bridges in Italy was their greatest exercise in futility. However, we loved to see them go over.

Monte Cassino and Cassino

The destruction by bombing of the monastery of Monte Cassino produced great political and religious repercussions. A note from my diary on February 14, 1944, while I was on Mount Lungo states: "Our boys are taking a terrific beating because of the refuge afforded the Germans using the monastery as an observation post, from whence they observe every detail of our lines. The wounded men that we see are very bitter at those responsible for keeping this huge building from being destroyed." Another note, February 15, 1944: "A sight to gladden the eyes today. At 9:00, seventy B-17s came over, very high, and knocked the monastery down. Then about a hundred B-25s and 26s bombed the same area, while some A-36s finished it off. We went up on the shoulder of Mount Lungo and watched the show. It was great." This bombing accomplished nothing useful. The Germans promptly moved into the rubble, cellars, and tunnels and continued to look down our throats. Our advances consisted of five to ten miles during this period and resulted in severe casualties and extreme hardship for our soldiers fighting in almost intolerable weather conditions. In January of 1944, the Thirty-sixth Division made a major attack across the Rapido River at San Angelo about three miles south of Cassino, but was thrown back and severely mauled. Subsequent to this, the Thirty-fourth Division attacked from the north of Cassino and reached the outskirts of the town, but was unable to hold its gains. Then the British and the New Zealanders tried to take the town of Cassino and the monastery, but failed. On March 15, 1945, the town of Cassino was utterly demolished by the greatest weight of bombs ever dropped on a target in the Mediterranean theater. Immediately following the bombing, an attack was made by the Indians, accompanied by a torrential cloudburst. The Germans still held steadfast. Next, the Poles were given the job of pushing the Germans out of Cassino and Monte Cassino. Same result. Finally, the French, under General Juin, outflanked Cassino by a brilliant pack-animal offensive through the Arunci Mountains, which lie between the Liri Valley and the west coastal plains.

The Poles made a final attack on the monastery. In short, it took us about seven months to go ten or twelve miles.

Our Divisions

Divisions consisted of about 15,000 men and meant little to the non–militarily oriented mind, but in combat there are marked variations in esprit de corps, determination, and performance. Our number one division, in my opinion, was the Third Infantry, commanded by Truscott and later by O'Daniel. They were used to spearhead many attacks and were skillful and determined fighters. Naturally, they had a high casualty rate, but their esprit de corps and pride were of the hightest order.

The Thirty-sixth Infantry was a hard-fighting, aggressive outfit made up in a large part by the Texas National Guard. They captured the Salerno Beachhead. They took many of the impossible mountains before Cassino, but it seemed to me their fighting spirit was never the same after they experienced the holocaust of the attempted Rapido River crossing below Cassino in January of 1944.

The Thirty-fourth and Forty-fifth Divisions were good, dependable, staunch divisions. The Forty-fifth surely kept us on the Salerno beachhead. In addition, the Forty-fifth held off the massive German counterattacks on the Anzio beachhead in February of 1944.

The Eighty-eighth was a fine division. Casualties were always high because of their aggressiveness. The Eighty-fifth Division was almost as good. The Ninety-first Division was not around long enough to make much of an impression on me.

In February of 1945, the Tenth Mountain Division was assigned to the Fifth Army. It lived up to its elite reputation and spearheaded the breakout of the Apennines into the Po Valley, racing on to the Dolomites.

The Rangers and Special Service Forces were first-rate outfits and did well. However, the Rangers were wiped out at Anzio in their delayed attempt to take Cisterna on Highway 7.

I have now the sad duty to report on the Ninety-second Infantry Division. This was an all-Negro division that arrived in Italy in the winter of 1944–45. They were put in the line on the west coast above Via Reggio in February of 1945. To test the division and as a diversion, they were ordered to make a probing attack. After a short advance, the Germans mildly counterattacked. To the Germans' amazement, the whole division threw down their arms and broke and ran, leaving all their equipment, guns, trucks, everything, and the road wide open to

Naples. The Germans suspected some clever Yankee trick and did nothing. Also, there were no German troops available to follow up this advantage. The Indians, who were in reserve, were rushed up and within forty-eight hours, had plugged the dike. They found all the guns and equipment unmolested. This whole debacle was hushed up by the army; even the *Stars and Stripes* made little mention of it.

An attempt was made to reassemble the Ninety-second Division, and each man that could be found was polled regarding his intention to fight. Only one-third expressed any willingness to do so. These blacks were sent back to the base area for use as service troops. This was the first and last time a black unit was used in the line. The Ninety-second Division was reorganized using the 442nd Regiment, the 100 Battalion (Japanese Nisei personnel), and a regiment with a good many division artillery units composed of the now redundant antiaircraft units of the theater. This reorganized division later pushed on up the coast to Genoa at war's end.

Medical Innovations

In the Mediterranean theater and particularly in the Italian Campaign, for the first time in history, a vigorous and successful attempt was made to salvage the critically wounded fighting men of an army. Col. Edward D. Churchill, professor of surgery at Harvard and surgical consultant to the Mediterranean theater, was responsible for keeping the surgical care of the wounded at a very high level. He saw clearly the need of large quantities of blood and arranged for large blood bank to be set up and blood gathered in base areas. He analyzed and wrote lucid directives regarding colon wounds, compound fractures, delayed primary closure of wounds, the necessity of doing wide and thorough debridement of wounds, and many innovations in war surgery. Penicillin, which we first obtained in limited amounts in November of 1943, helped to reduce the incidence of infection, particularly gas infection, to a remarkable degree. And, finally, Colonel Churchill made sure that the more seriously wounded were treated by competent and well-trained surgeons. His memoranda regarding these matters materially changed the army's previous concept of care, and his directives were used as models in both the European and Pacific theaters.

In contrast to the clean, healing wounds of most Americans, the Germans and also the Italian civilian physicians, expected and almost universally had purulent, chronic, septic wounds that often resulted in unnecessary fatalities.

With the use of helicopter evacuation of the wounded, it seems unlikely that the major surgery very close to the front lines that we did during World War II will be necessary in subsequent wars. This has been true in Korea and Viet Nam and will likely be so in the future.

Friendships

War is universally regarded as a frightful, horrible, senseless, and inhumane thing with its tremendous loss of life, dreadful injuries, useless waste of resources, and the disruption of families and lives. Yet there is no experience in life as great an adventure. The hardships, discomforts, dangers, fears, and disasters are compensated for by the camaraderie, interdependence, humor (mostly of a low type), bitching, and freedom from the petty aggravations and decisions of civilian life. Friendships made under combat conditions are very real and lasting; these conditions have a way of separating the men from the boys, the stuffed shirt from the real article.

As Lyman Brewer, in a recent publication (*Annals of Surgery, 197*, March 1983) so succinctly put it: "The 2nd Auxiliary Surgical Group is close to my heart, for the bonds of friendship hammered out on the anvil of front-line medical military service are as lasting as if they were forged of steel."

These great friendships were sustained and even deepened by the formation of two unique postwar organizations: (1) The Excelsior Surgical Society and (2) The Second Auxiliary Group Surgical Society.

Toward the end of hostilities in Italy, several of the army consultants on leave at the Excelsior Hotel in Rome, reinforced by appropriate drinks, discussed the formation of a surgical society, the members being selected surgeons of the Mediterranean theater. Preliminary plans, under the benign guidance of Eldridge Campbell, involved naming the society (inevitably the Excelsior Surgical Society), selecting seventy-five surgeons for membership, and naming Dr. Edward Churchill The Honored Member. Also, plans and organizational data were discussed at a preliminary meeting in New York in the fall of 1945, and the first formal meeting was held in Boston in October of 1946, with an astonishing number of the membership attending. Thereafter, the annual meeting was held just prior to the American College of Surgeons meeting. With the wives of the members wholeheartedly and enthusiastically attending, the meeting was held at various lovely resorts, such as Pebble Beach, Broadmore, Ojai Valley, Sea Island, Pinehurst, Rome, Italy, and Maui, Hawaii, to name a few. Despite markedly declining membership due to natural attrition, the meeting is still being held annually, with a handful of white-haired, tottering, old members keeping the memories and friendships alive. In 1979, the membership donated enough funds to support an "Excelsior—Edward D. Churchill" lectureship to be given annually at the interim American College of Surgeons meeting, presumably in perpetuity.

The Second Auxiliary Surgical Group Society, consisting of all the officers and nurses, was organized in New York in October of 1946. Gen. James H. Forsee was unanimously and gleefully elected secretary and treasurer, having to do all the work. He did an outstanding job and was reelected annually until his untimely death in the 1950s. The society has met every year in conjunction with the American College of Surgeons annual meeting. Attendance has been remarkable over the years, due largely to the efforts of George Sehlinger of Louisville, Kentucky, who has been forced, by unanimous acclamation, to function as secretary for the past twenty-five years. During one year, we elected him president, vice-president, and secretary-treasurer, all at the same time. He alone has kept this organization going happily over all these years. During the first few years after World War II, this meeting was characterized by uninhibited celebrations by its members. The large suite in the headquarters hotel, an open bar operating day and night, and the joy of meeting old friends led to some real bashes, lasting almost all night at times. Unfortunately, aging has taken its toll, and in recent years more restrained celebrations are enjoyed by the survivors.

In conclusion, I consider my assignment to the Second Auxiliary Surgical Group, and many subsequent duties as part of it as some of the great experiences of my life.

Chapter VIII
Italy Revisited

On July 2, 1975, the Excelsior Surgical Society joined Gen. Mark Clark's Fifth Army Headquarters reunion group in Rome to celebrate the "Thirtieth anniversary" of the liberation of Rome (actually thirty-one years and one month). The populace of Rome ignored its "liberators," but the Italian and American officialdom nicely celebrated our return, with elaborate receptions and parties at the lovely Barberini Palace and at the home of U. S. Ambassador Volpe—the Villa La Pariola. A special up-front section was reserved in Saint Peter's Square for the Fifth Army by the Vatican to be blessed by Pope Paul VI during the Holy Year Celebration.

On the Fourth of July, our group met and made a pilgrimage to the Anzio American cemetery, where some 8,000 American soldiers lie buried. The cemetery is a beautiful place: A lovely central airy building has commemorative maps and pictures done in tile and many names inscribed on walls, including Johnny Adams's name on the list of persons missing in action. Stretching out from the central building was endless rows of beautiful white marble crosses, each listing the dead soldier's name, hometown, and army serial number and the division or other outfit with which he was fighting when he was killed. The cemetery is impeccably kept, with well-tended shrubs, flowers, and grasses. I must admit to a certain melancholy on seeing the final resting place of so many fine young Americans.

A fitting commemorative ceremony was held at noon, with representatives from all the various nationalities that had taken part in the Italian Campaign participating. General Clark gave the formal address and placed wreaths in honor of all the nations represented.

With Charlie Rife, his wife, Evelyn, my wife, and Dr. Peter Graffagnino (who was a battalion surgeon with the Forty-fifth Division who was captured at Anzio and wound up in a German POW prison camp in Poland), I rented a car and took a nostalgic trip down Highway 6 to Cassino, the Rapido River, and the recently rebuilt Monte Cassino Monastery. We found that the Poles had constructed a gorgeous cemetery on the ridge running northwest of the monastery. We then went on the now four-laned tunneled highway to Venafro and up in the high mountains back of this town to a small chapel where Graffagnino had had his battalion aid station in the early winter of 1943. Circling south around Mount Rotunda, we visited Presenzano and Mignano, which had been entirely rebuilt. Then up to the Horseshoe Bend on Mount Lungo where the same pasture and house that was the site of our hospital in January of 1944 remained unchanged. The Italians had built an elaborate cemetery on the southern slope of Mount Lungo, but we did not have time to visit it. And so back through the Arunci Mountains through Itri and Terracina and Cisterna, and through the Alban Hills back to Rome. The height and ruggedness of the mountains the infantry had to take in the winter of 1943 and 1944 astounded the two ladies, and they couldn't believe we had taken them! I almost shared their beliefs.

Our annual banquet was held in a wonderful restaurant with the improbable name of "The Pink Elephant." Professor Piero Valdoni, who was now emeritus professor of surgery at the University of Rome, gave the Churchill Lectureship at this occasion.

After the Fifth Army's final banquet at the Excelsior Hotel, the Rifes, Peter Graffagnino, and the Wolffs rented another car and spent eight days touring the back roads of central and northern Italy, and southern Switzerland, visiting a good many sites recalled from 1944 and 1945. Driving up to the guarded gates of the Villa D'Este, in very informal clothes, we were admitted when I explained my previous occupancy. Entering the main hotel, we encountered the concierge. He acted a bit haughty until Dr. Graffagnino explained that I was the former "Il Commandante" of the place during World War II. The concierge at once became most effusive and cordial and could not do enough for us. It seems that he was employed in the kitchen during World War II and remembered me well. We rehashed old times for quite some time, and he bestowed upon us various gifts and souvenirs and told us to go wherever we liked, which we did. Thd old wooden operating pavilion had been demolished and removed; my private villa was unchanged. The grounds and gardens were superb, quite a lovely place.

There are several things about this return trip that impressed me: (1) The complete restoration and removal of all traces of the destruction of war. (2) The network of Autostrada (except in the back country roads), changing the whole geography of the landscape. For example, the Autostrada between Bologna and Florence goes through the Apennines so gradually that one hardly realizes that one is crossing a rugged mountain range. The remarkable Radicosa and Futa Passes have simply disappeared. (3) The horrible smog of the Po Valley. Instead of being able to see completely across the Po Valley from the Apennines to the Dolomites (fifty miles), one now is fortunate to see objects one-quarter of a mile distant. All else is blotted out by the smog. (4) The attitude of the presentday Italians toward their "Liberators" of World War II. Any Italian under forty years of age shows no interest in the ancient history of World War II, regarding it with no more concern than the invasion of Hannibal in 218 B.C. However, if one asks any Italian over fifty years of age about World War II, one strikes a memorable light and is instantly regaled in detail with the hardships, adventures, and personal experiences of that particular Italian during World War II. They remember, all right!

Appendix
Courage of Wounded Soldiers Remarkable, U.S. Surgeons Say, by Lee McCardell, War Correspondent for the *Baltimore Sun* ©

With the Fifth Army Before Cassino, March 8 (By Cable)—The Army's smoothest-riding vehicles are its meat wagons–motor ambulances.

They have more springs. But no GI is anxious to ride back from the front in one as a patient, not even with what he calls "a $1,000,000 wound," an injury that will disqualify him for futher combat without handicapping him too much in later life.

A soldier wounded in action gets first aid on the battlefield or at a battalion first-aid station close behind the battle line. If he needs hospital treatment he is taken farther back to a collecting station, where a "meat wagon" picks him up and carries him to a clearing station.

Gets Careful Checkup

There the Army doctors look him over carefully. If he is still fit to travel he gets another ambulance ride to an evacuation hospital, but if he's hurt so badly that he needs immediate attention he goes to the nearest field hospital, which may be just across the road.

You see some of the worst and some of the best sides of war in a field hospital. The worst, because only the most seriously wounded are brought in here. The best, because the soldiers never complain. Sometimes the field hospitals get wounded Italian civilians. At the first sight of the white-gowned surgeons they begin screaming:

"Mamma mia! Madonna!"

But wounded GIs, however great their pain, never complain. Army doctors say they are the best patients in the world.

Group Works in Teams

Most surgery in field hospitals here is done by surgical teams, consisting of a surgeon, an assistant surgeon, an anaesthetist, a woman surgical nurse and two enlisted men rated as surgical technicians. Teams are assigned from their parent outfit, the Second Auxiliary Surgical Unit commanded by Col. James H. Forsee, to whatever field hospital may need them.

Hundreds of the most seriously wounded Americans in the battle for Cassino have been treated at Field Hospital No. 11, Third Platooon, where one of the surgical teams is headed by Major Luther Wolff, of Roanoke, Va. The Third Platoon's long hospital tents with the big, red Geneva crosses painted on their tops are pitched on muddy flats enfolded by bare, stony hills a few miles from Cassino.

Shells Whistle Overhead

Incoming and outgoing shells whistle over the hills "like somebody tearing silk" to Major Wolff's ears.

In one corner of the pyramidal tent where he and his assistant, Capt. Trogler F. Adkins, of Durham, N.C., and their anaesthetist, Capt. Charles W. Westerfield, of Columbia, Miss., sleep when they can find time, there's a three-man foxhole which none is too brave to use when incoming shells burst too close—though the hole isn't inviting just now, being filled with muddy rainwater.

The flats are awash with mud and water. You have to wipe mud off of the roadside sign to read the hospital's designation. But the tents are ditched and to wounded GIs, tired and wet and muddy, particularly those brought back from the front at night in meat wagons over rutted mountain roads, Field Hospital No. 11 is a little bit of heaven.

Tents Well Lighted

Its tents have a hard-packed floor of ash and gravel and are dry. Coal, the only coal for miles around, burns in the tents' tin stoves. The tents are brightly illuminated inside with shaded electric lights. There are sheets, and pillows in pillowcases, on the cots and the covers are folded back by army nurses, the closest American women to the front.

Wounded GIs, carried in on litters and lined up in the admission tent, blink gratefully in its warm light while waiting their turn in the adjoining operating tent where the doctors, working 16 hours at a stretch on a seemingly endless belt of patients requiring as many as

60 blood transfusions in one day, lose all trace of time.

"There's nothing like it in a civilian hospital," says Westerfield. "You almost never run into cases as serious and complicated as the ones we get. The worst banged up patient of a peacetime automobile accident is in Paradise compared to the shot-up GIs they bring us. A lot of them look hopeless before you start, but somehow they often hang on. They just won't die. These GIs—I tell you, they're remarkable!"

Shellfire Wounds in Head

Deep chest or belly wounds, multiple injuries, amputations, anything and everything in the way of a surgical case that can't wait until the soldier has been evacuated farther back fall to the lot of the surgical teams. About 70 percent of the injuries they handle have been caused by shellfire, about 25 percent by small-arms fire, and the rest by mines, bombs, grenades, etc.

The surgical team carries its own surgical chest. Other supplies and equipment like dressings and sterilizing apparatus are provided by the field hospital. Masked and gowned, three doctors, their nurse, Miss Frances Mosher, of South Bend, Ind., and two technicians, Corporals Donald Scott, of Des Moines, Iowa, and Lloyd Dunlap, of Grenada, Wis., work by electric lights reflected down on the operating table from a tin trough suspended on overhead wires. Cold winter weather has put to sleep the Italian flies which used to crawl down the surgeons' gloves into open wounds last summer. Shellfire doesn't bother the surgical teams as much as it does their patients, who want to get off the operating table, litter or cot and down closer to the ground when the shell bursts near. One of the greatest inconveniences to surgeons is high wind, which sets hospital poles to weaving and keeps lights rigged from the poles jigging about.

From the operating tent, wounded soldiers are carried into the ward tent where they are under the charge of six army nurses, the Misses Ina Henke, of Stanley, Wis.; Virginia Neel, of Roanoke, Va.: Emma Jean Hall, of Morgantown, W. Va.: Pauline Skaloss, of Martin's Ferry, Ohio; Marian Miller of Portsmouth, Ohio, and Marjorie Houghton, of Boston. In the eyes of the wounded GIs they're the most beautiful nurses in the world.

Makes Fudge for Patients

The nurses don't go in for any starched uniforms or perky white caps. They wear olive drab shirts, slacks and stout mud-resisting shoes.

But they know how to make a bed, how to pat a pillow and how to do a hundred and one other little things that a woman nurse can do to ease your pain. At night when she's off duty, Miss Neel sometimes makes fudge for her patients. She has an understanding with the hospital mess sergeant who knows where to get the stuff she needs.

There are no luxury patients in this ward. One soldier they call "Tennessee" had lost his right arm and his left, both legs and chest riddled by fragments of a shell that came through the roof of the house where he had taken cover during the battle. On a cot next to him lies a kid from Mount Vernon, N.Y., who is pretty bitter about the shrapnel that tore one of his legs and his chest to pieces. He was in a foxhole waiting to come out of line when a shell burst over him.

Feels like Switchboard

Despite their determination not to die, not all of them pull through. One kid who caught it in the chest, belly and both legs, the head, right hand and left foot and then was burned never had a chance. But they never give up and they always see the funny side of things. A wounded soldier who is getting oxygen and a blood transfusion while half a dozen other rubber drainage and suction tubes are hitched to various parts of his mangled anatomy looks up at Major Wolff and grins and says, "Gee, Doc, I feel like a telephone switchboard."

"You can't lick these GIs," says Major Wolff. "You can't say enough good things about them. They're the most wonderful guys in the world. I don't know how they take it, I know I couldn't."

Major Wolff is "Geechee," Captain Adkins is "Troke" when they get together in their own tents late at night or in the dark of early morning. Troke shakes down the fire in the tin stove, Charles makes coffee in a German mess-kit pot and Geechee slips around to the cook tent to forage for flour. They've got a can of bacon grease and somewhere they've found a chicken. Charlie is going to fry it.

"Like I've seen my wife frying chicken at home," he says.

They're been together now for a long time. They're got a lot of stories. About the time they set up an operating table in a clearing station at Salerno. About the time Margaret Bourke-White, the gal photographer, thawed out suddenly during a visit to their hospital when a shell burst sent fragments through the mess tent. About the time in Sicily when Gen. George Patton, leading a tank column, overtook their outfit on the move on the road and hollered:

"Get those medics out of there and let my killers past!"

There is, too, of course, a good deal of talk about going home, where

Geechee has a wife, a small daughter and two sons, one of whom he's never seen, where Troke has a son he's never seen and Charles has a boy 9 months old. Charles fries chicken without flour. Geechee hasn't been able to find any. Shells keep tearing across the hills. One coming in bursts. Troke says:

"Jerry really gooses you at times."

But the chicken Charles fries up tastes damn good.

Glossary

AA—Antiaircraft.
AAOP—Antiaircraft observation post.
APO—Army post office.
Duck Feet—Beach landing.
DUWK—Amphibious truck.
Evac—Evacuation hospital.
Triage—The sorting out and classification of casualties to determine
     priority of need and proper place of treatment.
Yocky-Docky—Ethyl alcohol, water, lemon powder, and sugar.

Aircraft

A-36—P-51 fighter plane equiped with diving wing slots
for divebombing.
Beanfighter—British night fighter plane.
B-17—U.S. heavy bomber, "Flying Fortress."
B-24—U.S. heavy bomber, "Liberator."
B-25—U.S. medium bomber, "Mitchell."
B-26—U.S. medium bomber, "Marauder."
C-47—"D.C.-3," cargo and transport plane.
F.W.—German fighter plane, "Foeke wolf."
L-5—Piper Cubs-Artillery observation plane.
M.E.—German fighter plane, "Messerschmidt."
P-38—"Lighting," U.S. twin boom fighter plane.
P-39—Bell "Aerocoba," U.S. fighter plane.
P-40—U.S. fighter plane.
P-47—U.S. "Thunderbolt" fighter plane.
P-51—U.S. "Mustang" fighter plane.
Spits—British fighter plane,"Spitfire."

Landing Craft

L.C.A.—Landing craft assault.
L.C.I.—Landing craft infantry.
L.C.V.P.—Landing craft vehicle and personnel.
L.S.T.—Landing ship tank.

Index

Forward surgery of the severely
  wounded, 174
Foxholes, 43

G

Gabellino, 107, 108
Gas alarm, 11, 12
Gas gangrene, 56
Grassetto, 104
Guignola, 130–35

H

Hawk, 108 et seq
Holtz, Colonel, 65

I

Il Giurgo Pass, 126
Intramedulary pinning, 172
Italian civilian hospital, 124
Italian field hospital, 54
Italy capitulates, 5
Italy revisited, 197–99

L

La Boheme, 87–88
Lake Como, 168–74
Lake Guarda, 163–67, 174, 175
Lama, 157–59
Last Supper, 176
Legion of Merit, 148, 150–51
Luftwaffen Lazarette, 107, 169–74

M

MacCardell, Lee, 79
Maddaloni, 23–28
Maison Blanche, *xxi*
Marcianese, 51, 56–58
Marnix, 3
Medical supplies, 32–33
Merano, 181
Mignano Gap, 55

Milan, 178
Mount Lungo, 65, 79, 197
Mount Maggiore Masif, 42, 50
Mount Vesuvius, 85, 86

N

Naples, 28, 48, 56, 154–56, 184–86
Naval firing, 5, 15
Ninety-fourth Evacuation Hospital,
  27, 28
Ninety-second Division, 205

O

Oran, 2–3
Orbetello, 103

P

Paestum, 5
Parma, 163–65
Peccioli, 114–15
Pisa, 121–22
Poggibousi, 120–21
Pomerance, 111
Pompeii, 61
Pope Pius XII, 145
Poretta, 156
Po Valley, 161–67
Presenzo, 37, et sig., 197
Purple Heart, 10
Purple Heart Valley, 55

R

Rabat, *xvii, xviii*
"Rabbit hunting," 97
Radicosa Pass, 134
Rangers, 50, 76–77, 203
Rapids River, 66–67, 197
Refrido, 128–30
Riva, 175
Rome, 101, 102, 117, 118, 144–47,
  183, 196, 197
Russian POWs, 105